To John
Happy Christmas xaring ι ι ιⴰ.
all my love
Irene
x x x x x
x x x ⴰ x

CW00923030

THE INDUSTRIAL ARCHAEOLOGY
OF CORNWALL

THE INDUSTRIAL ARCHAEOLOGY OF THE BRITISH ISLES

Series Editor: E. R. R. GREEN

Derbyshire, by Frank Nixon
The East Midlands, by David M. Smith
Galloway, by Ian Donnachie
Hertfordshire, by W. Branch Johnson
The Lake Counties, by J. D. Marshall and M. Davies-Shiel
Lancashire, by Owen Ashmore
Scotland, by John Butt
Southern England (second edition, revised), by Kenneth Hudson

ASSOCIATED VOLUMES

The Bristol Region, by R. A. Buchanan and Neil Cossons
Dartmoor (second impression), by Helen Harris
Gloucestershire Woollen Mills, by Jennifer Tann
The Peak District, by Helen Harris
Stone Blocks and Iron Rails, by Bertram Baxter
The Tamar Valley (second impression, revised), by Frank Booker

OTHER INDUSTRIAL HISTORY

The British Iron and Steel Industry, by W. K. V. Gale
The Early Factory Masters, by Stanley D. Chapman
The Engineering Industry of the North of Ireland, by W. E. Coe
The History of Water Power in Ulster, by H. D. Gribbon

All these books are in uniform format

The Industrial Archaeology of

CORNWALL

A. C. TODD

PETER LAWS

DAVID & CHARLES : NEWTON ABBOT

ISBN 0 7153 5590 2

This book is dedicated with affection to
Rex Wailes
who has inspired so many to the study of industrial history

*Set in Imprint, 11pt 2pt leaded
and printed in Great Britain by
Latimer Trend & Company Limited Plymouth
for David & Charles (Publishers) Limited
South Devon House   Newton Abbot   Devon*

Contents

List of Illustrations

PLATES

IN TEXT

PART ONE

CHAPTER ONE

Cornwall and the New Archaeology

CORNWALL today is a mecca for tourists, a canvas for painters, and a dream-world for industrial workers on the edge of retirement. Those who may buy their cottage on a headland or in a valley that winds down to the sea often little realise that Cornwall, from 1760 onwards, was as industrialised as the Midlands and the North of England they have left behind. For almost two hundred years it was one of the most important metal-mining areas in the world and the setting for tremendous enterprises in the world of engineering, its blue skies shrouded by the smoke from a thousand chimney-stacks, and its wildlife in the fields, moors and lanes disturbed by the roar and clatter of machines. J. H. Collins in his *The Miner in Cornwall and Devon* (1897) wrote in a powerful and dramatic way that Cornwall had yielded over £200 million worth of tin and copper; that hundreds of shafts had been sunk and thousands of miles of galleries driven with forests of timber erected for their support; that mountains of ore and rivers of water had been brought to the surface; and that fleets of ships were required to bring the coal to feed the boilers and smelters. At the height of the county's economic and industrial supremacy—from about 1830 to 1860 when copper was supreme—over 600 steam engines were at work for the winning of tin, copper and china clay, while scores of foundries manufactured these giants of the art of pumping, some of them for the silver mines in Mexico and the gold mines of Australia.

Behind the machines and the men who built and operated them stood a small army of distinguished Cornishmen who were to make this the most creative epoch in Cornwall's long history, men who were to earn a reputation that was both national and international. The list of their names is a long one, and many of them appear in the pages that follow: Davies Gilbert, superb technocrat, mathematician and politician, the promoter of the natural genius of engineers of the calibre of Richard Trevithick and Jonathan Hornblower, and President of the Royal Society after that other great Cornishman he discovered, Sir Humphry Davy; Francis Trevithick, the son of Richard, who became the first locomotive engineer of the LNWR; Arthur Woolf, Matthew Loam, William West and other great engineers; John Harvey, first of a dynasty of ironfounders at Hayle; the Fox family with their impressive foundry at Perran, begun largely through the expertise that had been built up over the years at Coalbrookdale in Shropshire; John Vivian who developed in Swansea one of the greatest smelting plants in Europe; Joseph Austin Treffry and his vast copper mines around St Austell; William Praed of Trevethow, banker and builder of the Grand Junction Canal between London and Birmingham; Sir Francis Basset, William Molesworth and other agricultural pioneers.

From their knowledge, skills, vision and inventiveness flowed an energy, enthusiasm and industriousness beyond compare. As elsewhere in England, under this frenzy of activity, population increased, not entirely because of the breeding of new strains to withstand disease or because of improvements in medicine, but because bigger families meant an economic investment in the labour market. In Cornwall from 1801 to 1861 the population nearly doubled, from 192,000 to 369,000. More working hands meant that other industries could expand and sustain their own growth as Cornwall continued to act as the world's main source of copper. Trade and industry bounded along as never before in spite of periodic slumps, as when the copper pinched out in the 1860s: Cornwall even attracted workers from other parts of England. The boom in mining affected other industries. Quarrying became a major industry as more granite and slate were needed for engine houses, foundries, mills, roads, viaducts, houses, shops, poor-law institutions, municipal buildings, schools, libraries, churches, chapels, and the new institutions that emerged with the new culture, eg the Royal Institution of Cornwall, the Falmouth

Polytechnic, the Camborne Literary Institution, the St Just Lafrowda Club, the Royal Geological Society of Cornwall, and the many mechanics' institutes. Between 1809 and 1908 over 350 miles of railway track were laid to keep trade and commerce on the move, while more than forty ports catered for the immense fishing fleet and seaborne traffic. Nine ports were created for the new industrial age: St Ives, Portreath, Par, Pentewan, Hayle, Newquay, St Agnes, Porthleven and Bude. To protect shipping, lighthouses of incomparable design were built by a small but élite class of stonemasons who risked their lives in nigh impossible seas to erect the Eddystone, the Wolf, the Longships and the Bishop.

Cornwall, hub of the mining world, pioneer of the high-pressure steam engine, home of a race of engineers, technologists and 'promoters', as the entrepreneur was called in those days, is now a very different county. Its railways and ports, except Falmouth, Par and Fowey, are in decline: Wadebridge has not seen a ship since 1962. Quarrying has almost disappeared. Foundries are almost extinct, Holman's in Penzance and the one operated by English China Clays at Charlestown alone living out some of their former greatness. Fishing is almost confined to Newlyn. Water-power has very nearly vanished: in the 1880s there were about 300 water-powered mills; today there are two. The manufacture of gas, first begun in Cornwall and covered by twenty-six plants, has ended. Brickmaking has altogether ceased. Hundreds of tanneries have disappeared, leaving only one. The former fuse-making industry, pioneered by William Bickford in 1831 and once so vital, is now no more, though ICI still make gutta-percha for the explosive industry in Kennal Vale within an old dynamite works. The preparation of arsenic, once the standby during periodic slumps in the metal industry and of great value to the cotton belt of the southern states of the USA, has also gone. China clay alone reigns supreme with its $2\frac{1}{2}$ million tons a year discharged through the ports of Par, Fowey and Charlestown. But in some respects tin, confined for some years now to two mines at Geevor and South Crofty, looks as if it might be moving towards a revival. For instance, Consolidated Goldfields Ltd at Wheal Jane, near Truro, has discovered a 5 million ton ore-body of tin, copper and zinc that had been left by former miners because nineteenth-century technology could not handle its problems of concentration. Even so, the smelting of tin now has to be handled in Bootle, for the Cornish smelting works have long since vanished.

Population grew steadily until the 1860s and then declined with monotonous regularity until the 1940s, as the following census figures show:

Year	Total Population Cornwall
1801	192,281
1811	220,525
1821	261,045
1831	301,306
1841	342,159
1851	355,558
1861	369,390
1871	362,343
1881	330,686
1891	322,571
1901	322,330
1911	328,098
1921	320,705
1931	317,968
1941	no census
1951	345,442
1961	342,301

The dynamism of industrial progress and mining brought about the enormous rise 1801–61, followed by the equally dynamic fall because of the mining collapse between 1861 and 1901. The collapse was caused by the pinching-out of copper ores and the discovery of larger and more easily worked deposits overseas, especially in Michigan. Tin was never strong enough to take up the slack; so the mining industry entered a depression from which it never recovered and the miners and their families had no alternative but to emigrate. The modern increase in population (the high figure of the 1951 census probably reflects temporary wartime personnel) is almost certainly due to the large influx of retired persons and the effects of increasing tourism.

Cornwall is smothered by the monuments, great and small, of its mighty industrial past: it is therefore an ideal workshop for a study of the forces that changed it out of all recognition. Many excellent and well-documented studies have been written about its economic development and decline, its wasting assets of copper and tin and the consequent changes in the social life of the people as they searched for another living overseas. This book, however, is an attempt to write its industrial history, not from archives and documents, but from ground level using as evidence the actual physical remains that today lie around in such profusion. Metal mining and the winning of china clay, for instance, only really come alive when the student sets his mind and his imagination to work among the confusion of ruins that he sees before him on the ground. To stand amid the chaos of such a complex as the Levant Mine in all its stark abandonment is to realise with a shattering effect the sheer immensity of the task that lies before him. The challenge, as he sits down among the wreckage, is two-fold: to see again the complex of buildings growing as they did before the eyes of the engineers and the craftsmen; and then to visualise the natural landscape as it was before they occupied it and adapted it to their own needs.

This is a very difficult task and will make heavy demands on the student's critical and perceptive abilities: it is no longer sufficient merely to identify a calciner, a buddle or a flue; it is now necessary to be able to reconstruct in the mind, and on the ground, the complete flow of production from the point where the ore was raised to the spot where it was shipped to the smelter. From the available evidence on the ground the student will find himself faced with many tasks and problems of identification and interpretation: the suitability of the site; the general arrangement and design of the plant and the sequence of erection (in the case of a mine this involves a consideration of the frequency of re-workings); the methods by which the ore was extracted, reduced, concentrated and refined; the kinds of machinery used; and even the types of housing for the miners. Mining tools may be found on a site and these will need to be identified, classified and dated, either by reference to a manufacturer's handbook or to an archaeological method that depends on the recognition of style, design and function.

The recording and investigating of sites, machines and tools are an essential part of social anthropology and historical archaeology and ought to lead to studies that are much needed: the design of chimney stacks and engine houses and the use of different building materials; the tools used for the working of slate and granite quarrying; the art of sinking and lining mine shafts with wood, stone and steel; mills and milling machinery; the design of concentrating tables, etc. Machines and tools migrated from mine to mine and from Cornwall across the world, as did the men who used and operated them: no one as yet has plotted the distribution of Cornish-designed engine houses that are to be found from Upper Michigan to Mexico. No one as yet has written about the emigration of the Cornish stamp-mill and accounted for its supercession by those from California and South Africa. Such studies are bound to raise some questions about the relationship between man and the machines and tools he used in an industrial age; and how he employed them to change the physical environment.

A real study of Cornwall as part of the researches of the industrial archaeologist should produce much of interest to the cultural geographer, who is concerned about changes in the landscape brought about by machines and about the origin and distribution of the techniques involved. The economic historian too cannot disengage himself from the technical processes that account for the rise of one industry or the decline of another. Since technology is the key to culture, it is almost axiomatic that the social anthropologist must admit to his studies the nature of the machines that have contributed to our complex industrial societies. Equally the industrial archaeologist has an important contribution to make to what might be defined as the aesthetics of industry: engine houses that take on the

Page 17   *Two of the most dramatic engine houses in Cornwall built just above the sea for the Crowns section of Botallack Mine, near St Just*

Page 18 (above) *The saving in 1935 of this historic Harvey beam engine of 1840 at Levant tin mine was the beginning of conservation of Cornish industrial monuments; now in the care of the National Trust; (below, left) Tregurtha Downs engine house built 1881–2 for an 80in engine from Copperhouse Foundry, Hayle; (below, right) East Pool rotary-beam winding engine made by Holman's Foundry, Camborne, 1887; now in the care of the National Trust*

appearance of Cornish chapels; granite stairways in mines that are as beautifully designed as any in a church tower; factories that were made to look like the coach houses of the gentry; chimney stacks that, for their mathematical precision of construction, bear comparison with the columns of a Roman temple; and crushing mills that one could easily mistake for part of a medieval monastery. There is all this and more for both the professional and the amateur in Cornwall, where a single capstan in a cove below the mining town of Pendeen led to the discovery that some Cornishmen spent their days winning tin from the darkness a thousand or so feet 'below grass', and their nights in searching for fish, choosing to name their cluster of cottages St Peter's Row.

CHAPTER TWO

Copper

IN the popular mind Cornwall has always been associated with the mining of tin, but it was copper which made the most spectacular contribution to the county's economic development, giving it an industrial and political power out of all proportion to its size. Copper was responsible for the building of its many foundries, railways and harbours: it converted the county from a land of poor agriculture and uncertain fishing to the hub of a revolution in industry that stretched from the Tamar as far as the silver mines of Mexico, even though its extractive life, compared with that of tin, was short. Copper was king only for 150 years or so, roughly from 1700 to 1870, whereas tin has been mined from about 200 BC and still is. Again, unlike tin, copper was never subject to periodic booms and slumps but, in response to the brass industry of Birmingham and the sugar industry of the West Indies, bounded along from a mere 2,000 tons of ore in 1700 to a maximum of 140,000 tons about 1860, followed by a steady decline as the ores pinched out, and cheaper and more extensive deposits were found in Australia, Cuba and America.

Vast profits were made by Cornish landowners turned entrepreneur by the dazzling prospects around them: the Bassets, the Vivians, the Lemons, the Williams, the Grenfells, the Fox family, the Pendarves', the Daveys, the Daniells, the Teagues and J. T. Treffry, the most brilliant of them all, inspired by the sole outsider John Taylor of Norwich, who was without doubt the leading figure in metal mining in the western world. In 1827 Penstruthal Mine and Wheal Beauchamp each netted £60,000 and Crinnis £84,000, the latter going on to make a total profit of £168,000 in only four years. Tresavean in 1833 finished the year's working with a profit of £60,480 and in eleven years yielded £350,000. Consolidated Mines reached almost

£500,000 in twenty-one years, Lanescot and Fowey Consols made £130,000 up to 1837, Wheal Alfred £135,000 from 1804 to 1815, and Carn Brea Mines £225,000 from 1834 to 1853. The profits from tin were never of this magnitude, though the losses often were.

Copper differs from tin in one other respect, namely that the archaeology of only a part of the industry can be seen in Cornwall, that of the raising of the ore. The smelting was carried out in South Wales where, in Swansea, can be seen the vast industrial complex now owned by the Yorkshire Imperial Metal Company, that was once the empire of the Cornish Vivians, Williams and Grenfells. Copper linked Cornwall and South Wales in chains of metal as tin never did. The reason was two-fold: Cornwall's lack of coal, for it was the only county where metal mining was carried on without local fuel; and the discovery that copper ores from one locality smelted more effectively when mixed with ores from other areas. This situation had been appreciated in the very early days of copper exploitation when the Society of Mines Royal in 1580 leased its mining rights in Cornwall to one of its shareholders, Thomas Smith, the Collector of Customs of the Port of London. The Perran St George Mine and Wheal Leisure, both in the parish of Perranzabuloe, can only be designated as the possible sites of this Elizabethan venture, but in one of the ruined halls of Neath Abbey one can still see the discolouration on the sides of the chimneys whose fireplaces were used as furnaces for the smelting of Cornish copper.

There was, however, one attempt to smelt copper in Cornwall that deserves mention. About 1755 John Vivian and his metallurgist, Sampson Swaine, because of their dissatisfaction with the price of ores at Swansea, formed the Cornish Copper Company for the smelting of ores at Hayle, where land was bought along the eastern inlet for the landing of coal. Though their smelter and rolling mills to produce sheet copper have long since disappeared, except for the name of Copperhouse, their improvements to the harbour to promote their business of supplying timber, iron and coal to the mines in the Camborne area are still visible: the canal with its retaining walls of blocks made of scoria (slag) from the smelter to allow larger vessels to come in on the tide alongside the Copperhouse wharves, and the tidal sluice gates which impounded the whole of the eastern inlet and kept the harbour free from silting. Another memorial of this venture, and built before the silting of the harbour and the sad experience of the Cornish Metal Company in its battle with Thomas Williams of Llanidan forced Cornish entrepreneurs to join the Welsh smelters, is the fine house above the harbour, Riviere House. The home of John Edwards, manager and principal partner of the Cornish Copper Company, it was originally built of scoria and with a roof of copper, under which a generation of future engineers were born. It was sold after the foundry closed down in 1867 (see also Chapter Five).

    Much evidence exists in South Wales to show the remarkable success of Cornish management in the exceptional skill needed for the smelting of copper ores. In 1803 Pascoe Grenfell went into partnership with Owen Williams, the son of Thomas Williams of Llanidan, and set up the Copper Bank Smelting Works at Swansea. About the same time John Vivian started smelting at Penclawdd, just west of Gowerton, where the remains of his canal, small harbour, furnaces and cottages for his Cornish workmen still survive. (Cornish families still live there in the village that is the gateway to the Gower Peninsula.) Then in 1809 he leased the larger and new Hafod Works near Landore, where he laid the foundations of his smelting empire along the Lower Swansea Valley, and where can be seen in incredible profusion his silver works, foundry and engineering works, copper works, manure works, sulphuric acid works, alkali works and spelter works. Separated from his copper works by a boundary wall 30ft high are the equally impressive Morfa Works of the Williams family from Scorrier, who went into partnership with Joseph Foster and traded as Williams, Foster & Company. If to these be added the extensive works of the Llanelly Copper Company just below the village of Bryn on the estuary of the Loughor, partly owned by R. A. Daniell, a rich merchant of Truro who also owned Roundwood Quay in Cornwall, it can readily be understood how it came to be that these Cornish entrepreneurs dominated the entire copper output of Britain and for a time smelted the copper for the rest of the world.

They snatched their opportunities as they came. The Cornish production of tin had been static for centuries, and the same might have been true for copper but for a growing demand for a wide range of copper, brass and bronze products (brass is a copper-zinc alloy and bronze is a copper-tin alloy) as coins, kitchen utensils, buttons, buckles, harness parts, guns and armour, etc. After 1760 copper was increasingly used for sheathing the bottoms of naval and merchant vessels, for boilers and tubes in steam engines and for vats in the brewing, distilling and dyeing industries. Then, helped by a falling off in the Swedish production of copper, Cornwall received a further bounty from the opening-up of the African market—slaves being exchanged for manillas, bangles, neptunes and salt-evaporation plants—and the growing demands of the new West Indian market in the form of copper bottoms and plates required for sugar boiling and rum distilling. For nearly 150 years Cornwall was to meet all these needs and its landscape became scored with so many adits to drain its ever-deepening mines, and connected with the Great County Adit the mouth of which can be seen near Bissoe, that it was said that they were as numerous as the branches of a tree.

Redruth and Chacewater Area

While it has to be remembered that many mines in Cornwall were producers of both copper and tin, the major sources of copper were distributed over clearly defined areas. The first to be considered is that of Redruth and Chacewater, where the proliferation of engine houses, buildings and burrows exceeds belief. The remains of the Tolgus group of mines (Wheal Tolgus, East Tolgus, South Wheal Tolgus, Great South Tolgus, Tolgus United, Great North Tolgus and Wheal Mary) lie scattered on the slopes of the valley down which the B3300 road Redruth–Portreath runs. Some of the greatest copper producers in their time, they accounted for a total of 148,860 tons of ore from 1825 to 1883. On the left of the road from Truro to Redruth, just beyond Chacewater, are the engine houses of one of the oldest copper mines, Great Wheal Busy, which disgorged 104,700 tons from 1815 to 1897, and where the first Watt engine was erected in 1777 to replace the old Newcomen engine installed by John Smeaton. Near the grounds of Scorrier House are the workings of Treskerby Mine (47,540 tons, 1815–32) that was associated with Wheal Chance, its site now only marked by Scorrier railway station. South of the village of Lanner on the Penryn–Redruth road was the most important mine in the whole area, Tresavean, which by 1819 was reputed to have sold over £1½ million of ore, in 1830 was the third largest producer employing 1,350, and in 1842 accepted the first man-engine in Cornwall, based on a similar engine used in the Harz mines in Germany. Adjacent to Tresavean are the workings of Penstruthal (59,500 tons, 1825–79), Trethallan (35,920 tons, 1837–61), Wheal Buller & Beauchamp (169,496 tons, 1821–56) and Hallenbeagle (30,580 tons, 1835–46). Between Chacewater and Redruth, and lying to the north of, and roughly parallel to, the main railway line, are the remains of Wheal Rose, Wheal Hawke, Briggan Mine and, most prolific of this group, North Downs, beneath whose shallow workings are supposed to be Cornwall's largest untapped deposits of tin.

It was these mines and their problem of getting their ores away to Swansea that led to the laying of the first tramroad in Cornwall, much of which can still be traced either in its bed or from its granite sleeper blocks. The best position for investigating it is to begin with the harbour at Portreath, once known as Basset's Cove, north of Redruth. Built by the Bassets of Tehidy and the Fox family of Falmouth to cater for their mines around Camborne and Illogan, the harbour was small and confined but well built to withstand the hammering from the sea as its present state of preservation reveals. The idea of laying a tramroad from there to connect with the copper mines around Scorrier and St Day seems to have originated with Davies Gilbert who had been with Trevithick in South Wales in 1804 when the latter had demonstrated for Samuel Homfray, the ironmaster, a modified 'Dragon' locomotive to haul 10 tons of iron from Pen-y-darren to the basin of the canal at Abercynon. This Welsh tramroad that Gilbert saw became the prototype for the Cornish one that was to link Portreath with Poldice Mine and others, and has become known as the Poldice Tramroad; William Wood, Homfray's agent, supplying Gilbert with specifications as to cost, materials and the need for an act of parliament. The Portreath Company was formed by the Foxes of Falmouth to lay the line and to lease the harbour from the Bassets; the head of the family, Lord de Dunstanville, laying the first rail in 1809. Completely horsedrawn and worked in all weathers, it was an undoubted success with its double cargo of copper ore and coal, though the road must have been far from smooth with its short lengths of L-shaped plates on granite sleeper blocks.

From Portreath itself, the bed of the tramroad can be easily traced from the north side of the harbour along what is now the footpath of the Portreath to Redruth road, and thence via Bridge, Cambrose, Mawla, North Downs, Scorrier Station and Killifreth to Poldice Mine. At the western end of the now derelict station at Scorrier, there is an interesting brick skew-arched tunnel that the West Cornwall Railway built in 1852 to carry their line over the then still-used railway. In Holman's Museum at Camborne, there is preserved an open waggon, grandiosely called 'the Director's Coach', discovered in 1936 by Mr W. N. Blewett of Camborne, and also exhibited is a section of the iron rails of this tramway, used extensively until about 1880. It is not shown as 'disused' on the 1876 Ordnance Survey.

The second mineral line to be constructed was the so-called Redruth–Chasewater Railway built by John Taylor to link together his mines in the parish of Gwennap, one of the richest copper regions of the Old World, and to provide an outlet to the sea in the south. Of his gigantic and fabulous Consolidated Mines (total output 442,493 tons, 1819–58) very little now remains except the millions of tons of 'deads' in the burrows stretching along the western side of the valley almost to Carharrack. Almost gone too are the last vestiges of the equally renowned United Mines (347,640 tons, 1815–61), abandoned for their copper about the same time as Consolidated. A ruined stamps engine house and a smaller house for an engine that pumped water for the use of Hocking's mighty 85in engine (its house was wantonly demolished in 1951) belong to the year 1869 when an attempt was made to unwater the vast underground workings in the search for tin. A similar fate has overtaken Wheal Maid, Poldice, Unity Wood, Wheal Jewell (drained by the Great County Adit), Ting Tang, Wheal Gorland, Wheal Damsel, and Clifford Amalgamated (notorious for its heat) apart from one of its engine houses.

But much survives of the mineral line that served these mines. In a sense it was a rival to the Poldice tramroad, in which the controlling influence belonged to John Williams of Scorrier who had failed to find the Consols lode. In his mortification because John Taylor had succeeded, Williams made strenuous efforts to prevent the new line being built to Redruth but to no avail. And so it happened that the line was financed by London business men, many of whom had already helped Taylor to reopen Consols, including members of the Martineau family, brewers associated with the Whitbreads. The Scottish engineer, William Brunton (1777–1851)—his son, also William, was the engineer of the Hayle to Portreath railway from 1840–7—was chosen to undertake the construction of the line from Redruth to the wharves at Devoran; later it was extended to Point Quay on Restronguet Creek on the river Fal. He used an unusual 4ft gauge, though not unusual in South Wales, and wrought-iron rails set in cast-iron chairs bolted to granite sleeper blocks. But his most important innovation was his reliance on edge-rails with flanges on the waggon wheels, a marked advance on the plate-way of the Poldice tramroad.

The most advantageous way—and for the paragraphs which follow I am deeply indebted to D. B. Barton, *The Redruth and Chasewater Railway 1824–1915*—to trace the path of this line, which from 1824 to 1854 relied on horse traction and then, until its closure in 1915, on locomotives, is to begin at Penpol, where nothing now remains of the tin-smelting works and where the old wharves have been built over.

At Point itself there are no traces of the railway (nor of John Taylor's lead smelter), but the bed can be easily followed alongside the road from Restronguet Creek to Devoran, a village of infinite charm now, but at one time busy with the ships that brought in the coal and iron for the nearby foundry of Perran Wharf and took out the copper. Today the wharf is marked only by a line of fine granite bollards but other buildings still evoke memories of past industrial activity: the company's offices, the shipping office, warehouses, stables, ore-storage hutches, workshops now used by the Devoran Women's Institute, and the engine shed that has been incorporated into a private house. The line crossed the Falmouth–Truro road, its path now marked out over a garden that is edged by some of the original wooden railings and by two granite posts to which were hung the level-crossing gate, the keeper occupying one of the houses on Carthew Terrace. It passed over a weighbridge, near which the weigh-house still survives, and so continued along the side of the road to Bissoe, under the stone arches of the viaduct that carries the Truro–Falmouth branch line and by the ruins of the Cornwall Arsenic Works in the heavily industrialised Carnon valley.

Just north of Bissoe the line skirts the edge of the ruins of William Conn's chemical works and then carries on towards Nangiles Mine, whose engine house can be seen above the railway embankment, and where the interchange loop can easily be detected. The best-preserved section of the line now follows, from just above Twelveheads almost to Carharrack, for the bed has hardly been disturbed and the sleeper blocks are still in position. Just above the burrows of Wheal Fortune, near Hale Mills, it lies in a deep cutting of some 30ft depth, traversed by a bridge made of iron rails with rocks wedged in between to form a floor. Swinging out towards Redruth along a ledge cut into the hillside, it drives through the mountains of burrows of Consolidated Mines and past the crumbling walls of engine houses and the base of what was once the clock-tower, and emerges in the open fields before reaching Carharrack. Just before it reaches Primrose Cottage is the Great Yard, where coal and supplies were stored, a granite compound of impressive height that is now part of a farm's outbuildings. While there is no difficulty in tracing the course of the line through the village of Carharrack, from there to Pennance it becomes a matter of conjecture and short distances, though at Pennance can still be seen the granite walls of the Pennance Yard, just beside the road. At the summit of Lanner Hill is the site of the junction where the Wheal Buller branch looped away near the ruined engine house of Pennance Mine (also known as Wheal Bloody Nose) and then comes a long curved cutting (part of which has been filled in) before the line drops in an almost straight line towards Redruth, where it becomes lost in the buildings of the outskirts of the town.

Redruth and Camborne

Nearby, immediately west of Redruth, lies another group of copper mines. Here, at 189/661405, one of the most productive mines had been Dolcoath (247,800 tons, 1815–1905) which at one time employed 1,266 persons, 10 engines, 7 waterwheels and a man-engine, but which is now barely distinguishable from the mass of rubble and slag that clutters up the valley. Alongside the present railway too are the burrows and shafts, and a stamps engine, of what was once the Carn Brea mines, which from 1833 to 1905 disgorged 237,000 tons of copper ore and 30,000 tons of black tin. Almost equally impossible to detect now are Tincroft (112,700 tons, 1815–95) roughly on the site of Carn Brea station; Cook's Kitchen across the Red River from Dolcoath (43,600 tons of copper and 8,860 tons of black tin, 1815–1905); and North Pool (47,670 tons of copper, 1845–67). Wheal Seton north-west of Tuckingmill has suffered a similar fate, but not the Basset Mines, East Pool, Agar and Great Condurrow, though indeed the latter's splendid engine house dates from an unsuccessful re-working from 1907 to 1913. The group of mines known as Basset were the most prolific, producing 384,740 tons of copper and about 50,000 tons of black tin between 1815 and 1915, particularly South Wheal Basset, North Wheal Basset and South Wheal Frances. Yet

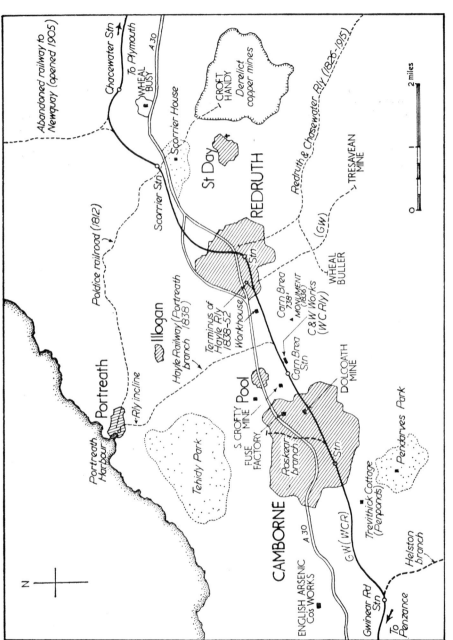

The Camborne–Redruth mining district

here again, the visible remains belong rather to the winning of tin, and especially the ore-stamps and dressing-floors at Carnkie, some of the most impressive in the whole of Cornwall; the engine house, stacks and other buildings of West Basset at New Stamps; and the magnificent engine houses of South Wheal Frances (which once contained Marriott's Cornish compound engine with two cylinders of 40in and 80in) and of Basset itself, erected in 1854 of superbly cut and dressed granite, of which only the bob-wall now remains. East Pool was an old copper mine at work in the eighteenth century that was restarted in 1835 with Wheal Agar to produce tin as well (91,320 tons of copper and 40,490 of black tin, 1835–1915), with some considerable quantities of arsenic and wolfram. Their remains lie close to the main A30 road, but again belong to the period of tin production: shafts and engine houses; the tall stack with the letters EPAL picked out in white brick, the company's initials and its arsenic brand-name; and two surviving engines, the 90in pumper just north of the road and the 30in winder, built for East Pool in 1887 and now standing beside the main road at Pool. Of the two final great copper producers, North Roskear (167,400 tons, 1816–74) and East Crofty (100,950 tons, 1832–53) both working ores of exceptional richness, little now remains, both of them having been absorbed by one of the two remaining tin mines in Cornwall, South Crofty.

It was to these mines that the Hayle Railway, the third and largest of the mineral lines in West Cornwall, was begun in 1834 and completed in 1838, being worked from the start by locomotives. With an authorised capital of £64,000, the company laid the track from Hayle harbour straight into the mining district of Camborne, by Dolcoath, Pool, Cooks Kitchen, Tincroft and the Carn Brea mines, and on to Redruth with one branch to Tresavean and another to the harbour at Portreath. Narrow gauge at first, and designed for the carrying of copper ore, coal, sand and general merchandise, it was realigned in 1843 for the carrying of passengers too from Hayle to Redruth.

At Hayle the railway began in Foundry Square and its passage through the town is described on page 99. After crossing the A30 by the Penmare Hotel, there was another level crossing over the road from Angarrack to Hayle near the crossroads at Loggan's Mill. The line then followed a well-defined embankment which crosses open fields for about a mile until it reaches the Angarrack incline with a gradient of 1 in 10. The mechanism for hauling wagons and indeed locomotives up and down has long since disappeared, but the cut in the bank is still visible, though difficult now to walk through, being completely overgrown with trees and bushes. From the summit of the incline the bed of the line can still be followed as it sweeps in a wide curve, now marked by a thick and broad hedge, to the point west of Gwinear Road station on the present main line where the track levelled out on its way to Camborne.

There were similar inclines at Penponds and Redruth, but it is the one at Portreath which today is deserving of the most attention: housing development at its summit threatens to remove its main distinguishing features. The Portreath branch of the Hayle Railway was opened in 1838 (traces of it can be seen from Illogan to the point where it comes out near the present main road from Camborne to Redruth, just about where the Railway Inn stands now) and carried so much coal and copper ore that a second basin had to be added to the harbour to relieve the congestion. This was caused by the very nature of the exposed position of the harbour and the delays of working the wagons up and down the incline by a system of stationary engines and ropes. The engineer was William Sims and measured drawings of his incline machinery can be seen in Holman's Museum at Camborne; but the holiday visitor to Portreath has no difficulty at all in picking out the deep cut in the cliff on the western side of the village that begins with a low-slung granite embankment of impressive proportions. At the summit all that is left of this engineering feat is a house named Incline Cottage.

Marazion and Leedstown

Through Hayle too went the copper output of mines in the district of Marazion, though very little remains of their buildings now. Binner Downs, near Leedstown, between 1819 and 1838 produced 51,100 tons with the aid of six engines and 390 workmen, but had to be shut down because of the heavy pumping and was never reworked because of the high costs. At Crowan, Crenver & Wheal Abraham (112,050 tons, 1815–70) was at one time the most productive of all the mines in Cornwall and in 1822, at a depth of 240 fathoms, the deepest mine in the county. Its three engine houses and other buildings have now vanished, and only long narrow burrows remain as the evidence of its once extraordinary activity. And nearer to Marazion itself, once the fifth largest producing-area, the same overgrown burrows, shafts, and an occasional bob-wall tell the same tale of the erstwhile prosperity of Wheal Prosper, Wheal Maid, Wheal Virgin, Wheal Rodney and Wheal Friendship.

The copper ore from these mines had to be carried in horse-drawn waggons to Hayle, a matter of no great difficulty along the flat valley floor.

Land's End Peninsula

For two great copper producers, Levant and Botallack on the coast north of St Just, the problem of haulage was much more acute, for here there was never any mineral line, although a route was surveyed under the Light Railways Act of 1896 by the engineer H. F. Stephens to connect with Penzance and to be called the Land's End, St Just & Great Western Junction Light Railway. Levant and Botallack were both copper and tin mines, and the complexity of their industrial remains makes it difficult to disentangle the copper workings from those of tin, so much so that the detailed account of the industrial archaeology of these two mines will be found in Chapter Four that deals with the winning of tin. Levant's output of copper alone from 1820 to 1930 was in the region of 130,400 tons and, if to this be added its tin, it will readily be seen how just was its claim to be without doubt the greatest of all the mines in the whole of the Land's End

Peninsula. It was originally worked for copper in the 1790s and came
into steady production in the 1820s, only being worked for tin after
1852. Even as late as 1910 it was still producing a sizeable quantity
of copper, at a time when it had reached a depth of 350 fathoms and
was extended a mile or so under the sea-bed.

Botallack was never as rich in copper as Levant but from 1815 to
1905 it produced 20,290 tons worth £220,701, and in the 1820s was
being worked entirely for copper.

Porthtowan to Perranporth

Further east beyond Hayle and Portreath, along the same rugged
and sharply indented north coast, several important mines in the
Porthtowan and St Agnes area faced the same problems of finding a
suitable harbour. A mile south-east of Porthtowan in the narrow
valley along the road to Scorrier, that looks for all the world like a
copper canyon in Arizona, are the engine houses of the United Hills
mines, later known as Tywarnhayle mines (86,800 tons, 1826–1906).
One of them is thought to have been among the last to contain a
wooden bob, and the other, higher up the slope of the hill, once
housed a 70in pumping engine. On the same road, where the valley
floor begins to widen, stand the ivy-covered house and castellated
stack of Wheal Ellen and the pit that was once Wheal Music, from
which copper-bearing rock was quarried, while on Porthtowan beach
itself rears the engine house of Wheal Lushington that has now been
converted, most seemingly and imaginatively, into a modern dwelling-
house. Further east at Chapel Porth, too small a cove to serve as a
harbour, is a group of mines known as Charlotte United, whose
engine house can be seen on the west side of the valley, while just
south of St Agnes Head is the apparently delicately poised house of
the Towanwroath shaft of Wheal Coates, high up on the cliffs. It was
an indifferent producer of both copper and tin, and remains of the
stamps and whim engine houses really belong to its tin period. Nearer
to Perranporth are the sites of Perran St George (105,830 tons,

1815–60), whose burrows extend from the cliff eastwards to the B3285 road, and Wheal Leisure (57,300 tons, 1829–40), whose surface works, dressing-floors and burrows once occupied what is now the main street in Perranporth. Both of these mines are the probable sites of the Mines Royal ventures in Elizabethan times. A short distance to the north of Perran Beach sits the whim-house of Penhale Mine, an early producer of copper and then, under the name of Penhale and Lomax Mine, of silver-lead ore and some hematite that came from the Perran iron-lode nearby.

The transport difficulties for these mines were extreme. As neither Porthtowan nor Chapel Porth were satisfactory inlets for harbours, the ore often had to be carted over rough tracks along the cliffs as far westwards as Portreath. An attempt was made to remedy this deficiency by building a harbour at the bottom of Trevellas Coombe near St Agnes, known as Trevaunance Quay, which was also to serve the tin mines of Wheal Luna, Wheal Kitty and Blue Hills. The narrow valley down to the sea still shows signs of this industrial complex: a succession of dressing-floors, waterwheel stamps and arsenic works in the overgrown leats and wheel pits; but little is left of the harbour. It was built of granite under the shelter of the western cliffs down which the ore was perilously lowered into waiting sailing boats from a platform and up which the coal from Swansea was hoisted. The line of this platform can easily be detected in the rock face and at the summit of the cliff the ore bins are still in place. The harbour, however, always received a pounding from the heavy seas and was destroyed in 1934; its broken wall is visible at low tide. Nevertheless, this tiny harbour served the district well until the coming of the railway.

A necessary digression at this point concerns the silver-lead mine of East Wheal Rose and its connection with the harbour at Newquay and its railway link to Par. In the parish of Newlyn East to the south of Newquay and north of the A30 road, lead was discovered about 1811 and a few years later Old Wheal Rose mine was started as a major undertaking, the output being large enough to warrant smelting

Page 35 (right) *A photograph taken in 1944 showing the bob of the 85in engine at Wheal Busy, made by the Perran Foundry. Despite an authoritative report to the Institution of Mechanical Engineers about this last engine of this foundry, it was broken up for scrap in 1945. The engine house, built 1848, still stands near Chacewater where the first Watt engine was set to work in 1777;* (below) *until 1969 the 'tailings' of Geevor Mine contained sufficient black 'slime' tin to make recovery economic. On the edge of the cliffs below the mine these 'round frames' were traditionally part of the tin streamers' equipment*

Page 36 (left) *The immense fluted iron chamber containing the counterbalance on the pump rod of the 90in beam engine made by Copperhouse Foundry, Hayle, in 1846 to the design of Thomas Wicksteed, who introduced the Cornish pumping engine to London's waterworks in 1838. This engine is preserved, with others, at Kew by the Metropolitan Water Board* (below) *tin stamps at Nancledra, powered by 18ft waterwheel from E. T. Sara's Foundry at Camborne c1890; 8 stamp heads lifted by wipers on a drive were operational until about 1948*

on the mine itself. Though traces of this have long since vanished, the house, Shepherds, that was built in 1819 for John Giddy, the manager of the mine and superintendent of the smelting house, still exists as a place of Regency charm and graciousness. The mine was abandoned about 1834 but almost immediately a new one was started at 185/ 836553, called East Wheal Rose, in a valley to the south of Penhallow Moor near the road from Newlyn to Mitchell. Today the view of its massive expanse of burrows and dressing-floors is one of the most spectacular in Cornwall, though most of them belong to the period of its disastrous reworking after 1881, especially the counthouse and the magnificent engine house. The latter, perhaps the finest of all, was designed by a London architect (like its sister house at Tregurtha Downs near Goldsithney) with an unusually high mounting for the 100in engine because of the danger of flooding, a lesson drawn from the unprecedented cloudburst of July 1846 which cost the lives of thirty-six miners.

Smelting at East Wheal Rose proved, contrary to previous experience, difficult, and H. L. Douch in his excellent *East Wheal Rose* comments, 'During the whole history of the mine the ores from East Wheal Rose were to be sold to the smelting firm which made the best offer.' Some of the early ores may have gone to Vivian's smelting works at Swansea through the recently (1833) completed harbour at Newquay, built by Richard Lomax at a cost of £10,000, consisting of a pier enclosing 4 acres and accessible to vessels of 700 tons in all weathers though not at all tides. In 1838 Joseph Thomas Treffry (Joseph Thomas Austen till he took his mother's maiden name of Treffry), the doyen of Cornish 'promoters', looking for a harbour on the north coast for the discharging of his china clay, bought Newquay from Lomax and set about its improvement, one of its drawbacks being that vessels had to ride at anchor in queues waiting for a favourable tide. So he started to build a 'lay-by' at Fistral Bay with a cutting through the cliff, where vessels might wait and shelter until the tide was right for them to enter Newquay. Though he died (in 1850) before it was finished, evidence of this imaginative enterprise

c

can still be seen at Fistral Bay. Treffry also had a lead smelter at Par which, after his death, was enlarged in 1866 with a stack 237ft high that was thrown down in 1907 and today is only remembered by the massive granite blocks about 30ft diameter that comprise its foundation. A year before he died, however, he had constructed a railway link between East Wheal Rose and Newquay (part of the line that subsequently went to Chacewater) and in February 1849 the first consignment of ore was loaded on one of his vessels at Newquay bound for Par.

St Austell

On the south coast near St Austell, where there was an important group of mines, copper shares with the china clay the distinction of opening up mineral lines and harbours. Here were St Austell Consols, north of Sticker, with ruined engine houses marking its site; the Pembroke Mine, started by John Taylor in 1815 and productive of 85,830 tons within the next fourteen years; and Crinnis and East Crinnis on the flats almost to the site of Par harbour. Little of them now remains apart from a few buildings and dumps near the shafts; but all their ores found their way to Swansea through the tiny harbour of Charlestown. Built in 1792 by Charles Rashleigh of Menabilly and designed by John Smeaton for the export of china clay, it has changed little in the last 150 years, and is still used for loading small vessels with clay destined for a European market. Then the only port between Fowey and Mevagissey, it could not cope with the load of both clay and copper going out and the load of coal and iron coming in, the latter consigned for the foundry just above the harbour, whose original buildings still house a flourishing industry and which will be described in detail in Chapter Three on foundries.

The creation of the port of Par was Treffry's answer, and it was bound up with his own considerable interests in Par Consols, whose site is just west of Par, and to a much larger extent in Fowey Consols (185/085560), high on the hill east of the road to Lostwithiel. The scale of his engineering achievements and the scope of his imaginative enterprise are not difficult to recapture today. Fowey Consols was the third greatest copper mine in the whole county and, together with Lanescot near Tywardreath, produced 382,910 tons of ore from 1822 to 1867. All that is visible now are the massive burrows and the shell of the engine house for his 80in pumping engine that was, without doubt, one of the finest ever built in Cornwall. William West of St Blazey Foundry, the chief engineer at the mine, also employed water power for pumping, installing no less than thirteen water-wheels, worked by the water brought from the moors east of Molinnis in leats that can still be traced. More spectacular are the beds of the two inclines he cut in the hillside, both of them double-tracked and tunnelled; one was 2,640ft long and rose to a vertical height of 280ft for taking coal and timber to the mine; the other was 1,127ft long and rose to a height of 80ft for despatching the ore to the basin of Treffry's canal below (p 133)—their cost was £2,818 and £630. The basin at Pont's Mill is now much overgrown with bushes but the course of the canal from St Blazey to Par and its lock can be walked most of the way. Perhaps it only requires a little imagination to reconstruct the passage of the ore boats, each loaded with 52 tons, pulled by horses. But Treffry also owned granite quarries in the Luxulyan valley and china-clay workings for which Par was to provide the outlet. So a 4ft 8in gauge tramroad was constructed from the canal basin, necessitating a further incline up the steep valley side to a height of 325ft above the level of the canal, and part of it cut through rock, a considerable feat of engineering if the incline is inspected today. Even more remarkable (p 90) is the fine and graceful ten-arch granite viaduct (built 1839–42) that carried the horse-drawn tramroad across the valley, and beneath it the flume along which flowed the water to work the waterwheels at Pont's Mill; surely the most abiding monument to the genius of Treffry apart from his own harbour at Par, today the busiest port in the south-west, shipping china clay to European ports at every tide. Par was an entirely artificial harbour, built on a reef, that took eleven years, 1829–40, to complete. It enclosed 35 acres and provided a breakwater 1,200ft long with wharves designed for the storage and shipment of copper from Fowey Consols. These have disappeared with the copper, but the harbour remains as Treffry's crowning achievement and will remain so, long after the last traces of his candle vats at Spit Beach have vanished.

Caradon Hill

In East Cornwall on the wild Caradon Moor north of Liskeard lie the remains of boom copper mines that luckily were discovered in the middle of the last century just when the mines in the west were petering out. Twenty-five of them with their complicated network of tramroads, they now add to the solitude of these grim yet beautiful moors, where the only signs of an industrial society are the silent signals that emanate from the slim mast of the ITV transmitter. Here are the impressive surface buildings, dressing-floors, engine houses and three stacks of South Caradon that produced 217,820 tons of ore from 1838 to 1885, the sett having been granted to Capt Peter Clymo about 1835. West Caradon (91,700 tons, 1843–86) survives only in its mammoth burrows. Craddock Moor (20,080 tons, 1856–74) paws the road from Minions to Doublebois. Gonamena, near the upper end of the Cheesewring branch line, can only muster part of an engine-house wall and a few remains of its original working for tin. East Caradon (54,000 tons, 1860–85) is now but a single huge burrow near the Upton Cross–Tokenbury road above the former track of the railway; and the same fate has befallen Glasgow Caradon Consols (37,530 tons, 1864–85), its site marked by a single burrow near a farm south of Upton Cross on the B3254 road. Time has been kinder to the Marke Valley mines (128,500 tons, 1844–90) where three engine houses of the Wheal Jenkin section remain near the former track of the railway, and two groups of engine houses of Marke Valley itself, together with waste burrows and dressing-floors near the stream at Upton Cross and older workings further down the valley. But perhaps the most interesting concentration of remains are those of Phoenix

United (186/266719) not forgetting the sole engine house of South Phoenix (186/263714) though, since it was a producer of both metals (82,690 tons of copper and 16,257 tons of black tin, 1853–87) it is not easy to separate the two industries on the ground, nor one re-working from another. For instance, the fine, huge engine house with its unusual square-based stack, built half of brick, is a relic of the last re-working for tin just before 1914 at the Prince of Wales shaft. At that time the tin lode was down to 1,200ft and 20ft wide but even so production was disappointing. Holmans of Camborne had installed an 80in engine, a two-speed horizontal engine, six heads of pneumatic stamps and Cameron pumps worked by compressed air. Now all have gone, even the engine that the Duchy of Cornwall bought and kept until 1930. An air of desolation and depression hangs over these windswept moors where once existed one of the largest concentration of waterwheels anywhere in Cornwall. Yet enough remains of the surface buildings of South Phoenix to bring alive the activity of men in their search for metals when William West of St Blazey was their engineer: the mill, open to the sky; the beds of tramroads; the counthouse; huge granite blocks with holes neatly drilled through them; a massive oak beam 2ft square that was part of the pit-work; a staircase of cut granite; the compressor rooms and forges; and the big rectangular depression, now overgrown with grass, that was once the pond.

The major problem for the Caradon mines was that of tramming the ores to the coast, and the nearest port was Looe. Already in existence when copper was struck at South Caradon in 1837 was the Looe Union Canal, opened in 1828, with its terminal basin at Moorswater (p 132). At first the copper ore had to be carted in waggons, over impossible tracks down to Moorswater so, in 1844, the Liskeard & Caradon Light Railway was laid as a joint venture by the canal company and the railway promoters. Its route from Moorswater passed through Tremabe, St Cleer and Crow's Nest to South Caradon, with two branches, one to Tokenbury Corner and the other over inclined planes to Cheesewring Quarry and Wheal Phoenix. Granite blocks were readily available from the quarry and the line, 8¼ miles long and of standard gauge, worked by horses, was quickly available for traffic within a matter of two years. In 1860 the canal was abandoned and the railway extended from Moorswater to Looe, the track being completely relaid so that it could be worked by three locomotives, *Cheesewring*, *Caradon* and *Kilmar*. To overcome the Gonamena incline so that the locomotives could work the entire length of the line to Phoenix Mine and Cheesewring Quarry the branch to Tokenbury Corner was further extended along the entire length of the contour line.

From Phoenix and the quarry, the bed of the railway, together with its interlocking system of tramroads, can be followed without much difficulty from the long curve round Caradon Hill, now dominated by the ITV transmitter, southwards to Upton Cross and Tokenbury Corner, thence declining through St Cleer to a cutting at 189/254669 and so to Looe Mills at 189/233648, where the ore wagons rumbled at the rear of the tollhouse. At Moorswater itself are the abandoned loco sheds with their inspection pits and, in a hedge, the firebox of one of the locomotives, reduced to the role of a public lavatory! Here too, near the impressive 150ft high modern railway viaduct and the gaunt churchlike piers of Brunel's original timber viaduct, can be picked out the remains of the canal basin, the towpath, part of the canal itself and a long wall with two arched masonry tunnels that comprised the wharves for the discharging of the copper ore. At Looe the wharves have been converted into a carpark, but tracking down the line of the canal from Moorswater to Looe is well worth the time, for it will bring the satisfaction of discovering on the ground the visible remains of its twenty-five locks. Equally enjoyable is to follow the bed of a tramroad that begins to the north-west of Caradon Hill and finishes about 189/235760 for no apparent reason in the middle of Kilmar Moor. Granite sleepers lie on the grass but today there is no other evidence of the purpose of this line, apart from that of serving quarries. As it terminates still pointing in the direction of the north coast towards Camelford and the North Cornwall Railway, one is tempted to speculate whether an alternative route northwards was being surveyed to reduce the high transportation costs of the long haul from the south coast to Swansea. In July 1884, Parliament in fact approved a proposal to join the northern extremity of this line to the NCR at Launceston, but it was never built.

Kit Hill and Gunnislake

One final copper area remains to be described, though briefly, since it has been the subject of an excellent survey by Mr Frank Booker in his *Industrial Archaeology of The Tamar Valley*: the Hingston Down mines in the neighbourhood of Kit Hill and Gunnislake. With Kelly Bray (15,251 tons, 1851–72), East Holmbush and Holmbush mines (42,900 tons, 1822–80), 2 miles north of Callington, they formed a group known as Callington United Mines working a richly mineralised zone of copper, tin, arsenic and silver-lead. Today their massive burrows and the remains of three engine houses, one still roofed, lie in a compact triangle of land marked off by pasture, woodland and the Stoke Climsland road. Hingston Down Consols (64,440 tons, 1850–82) is revealed by its unusual engine house that has its roof surrounded by a parapet. To the south-east along the road from Harrowbarrow to St Ann's Chapel are the dumps of the Prince of Wales mine (10,845 tons, 1865–1908). To the east are the stack and engine house of Gunnislake Old Mine, almost a part of Gunnislake itself for the village grew out of and around the mine. And nearby is the great Gunnislake Clitters, prospected in the 1820s by the Foxes of Falmouth—as was Gunnislake Old Mine by their rivals, the Williams family of Scorrier. Between Chilsworthy and Gunnislake itself lie the physical remains of this giant producer that brought to the surface 33,310 tons of copper between 1860 and 1904, as well as some tin, umber, wolfram and arsenic: two engine houses, dumps, flues, dressing-floors and a treatment mill. Its arsenic, produced from mispickel which occurs in association with copper ores in response to the demand for insecticides for the cotton lands of the

United States, was treated at the Greenhill works of the Cornwall Chemical Company at Gunnislake, its immense stack halfway up the hillside a conspicuous feature of the landscape. Three other copper mines, though limited producers, merit attention: the ruins of Calstock Consols near a disused cutting of the old East Cornwall Mineral Railway west of Calstock; the engine house of Okel Tor east of Calstock and its line of flues and stack, which were part of its arsenic works; and the engine house of Cotehele Consols, deep in the wooded Danescombe Valley, to the west of the village.

In the same area tin mines of considerable importance were also worked for copper. Oldest and richest of these was Drakewalls Mine at the summit of Gunnislake Hill (5,344 tons of black tin and 2,015 tons of copper ore, 1852–97), where can be seen the ruins of arsenic furnaces, the stack and building that housed the crushing stamps, and two engine houses, one for the pump and the other for the whim. At Luckett, north of Kit Hill, sprawl the remains of Wheal Martha, later known as New Great Consols: the stamps engine house, a crusher whim house, the 80in pumping engine house, and the arsenic flues extending up the hillside almost to Monk's Corner, terminating in a stack. Finally, at the very top of Kit Hill, is the spectacular 85ft tall stack which is all that remains of Kit Hill Great Consols and its engine houses; with its square pedestal base and lipped top, thought to have been insisted upon by the Duchy of Cornwall to give it the appearance of a monument, it now continues in that role and is preserved and maintained by the Duchy.

The transport problems on these barren moors were not more difficult than those on Caradon Hill, while there was also the distinct advantage of being not too far away from the Tamar and the open sea. Yet the hazards of poor tracks up and down the steep hills for the vast army of horses that pulled the ore and coal waggons to and from the awaiting quays at Calstock were real enough. So busy was the traffic, together with the other cargoes of timber, iron, granite, lime and agricultural produce, that it was clear that the only answer was a railway. So in 1863 five of the directors of the Tamar Coal, Manure

& General Mercantile Company, which had extensive wharves on the Tamar, proposed a scheme to build the Tamar, Kit Hill & Callington Railway, though it was not completed until 1872, when it operated under the name of the East Cornwall Minerals Railway. Seven and a half miles long and of 3ft 6in gauge, it began at Williams' Quay, Calstock, then leased by the Vivians of Swansea, and this is the best point now for anyone who wishes to follow its track as far as Kelly Bray, for it never reached Callington. At Calstock the lines of the 1,oooft of quays are well preserved; the granite quay was near the Danescombe Hotel and the copper quay was on the site of the present recreation ground. Above the quays the track of the rope-worked incline is still visible and, at its summit, an abandoned water tower and repair shop. From here, where the locomotives took charge, the bed of the track can be followed most of the way past Drakewalls Mine, Gunnislake, Pearson's Quarry, Greenhill arsenic works, Gunnislake Clitters Mine, then along the flank of Hingston Downs to below Kit Hill where an inclined tramway connected with the granite quarries, and so finally to Kelly Bray Mine where the line terminated.

Although the story of copper in Cornwall ends here, it is not the finish of the ore's history in the South West, for the lodes are no respecters of rivers and boundaries established by parliamentary commissions. In Devon the lode that began its course in Cornwall produced an ore shoot that sparked off the biggest copper mine in Europe, Devon Great Consols. But for an account of its industrial remains, its framework of tramroads and inclines from Morwellham Quay, the Tavistock Canal of John Taylor and the foundry in the same town, the reader is referred again to the competent survey and interpretation by Mr Frank Booker in *The Industrial Archaeology of the Tamar Valley.*

CHAPTER THREE

The Foundries

THE impressive development of the copper mines and the need for machinery inevitably led to the establishment of iron foundries, though in the days of the supremacy of Boulton & Watt very few seem to have been capable of building complete engines or of casting and boring large cylinders. But when by 1800 the patents of the Midland firm had run their course and Cornish engineers at last came into their own, their foundries rapidly earned for themselves the reputation of being some of the best in the world, their products exported to France, Spain, South America, Mexico, Australia, the West Indies and South Africa.

By far the most important was that of Harvey & Company of Hayle, established by John Harvey (1720–1803) but, since the entire economic prosperity of that port depended on the foundry's policy and products, its history will be found in the chapter on Hayle along with that of its rival, Copperhouse Foundry. Almost equal in importance was Perran Wharf Foundry, established in 1791 on a tidal inlet of the Fal estuary by the Fox family of Falmouth together with their partners Peter Price, the Tregelles families of Penryn and Falmouth, Thomas Wilson a copper smelter, John Gould a doctor of Falmouth, and William Wood an ironmaster from Swansea. Peter Price, born in Southport in 1739, was their iron technician, learning his craft at Coalbrookdale and then at the newly opened Carron foundry in Scotland, before joining the Perran foundry from London where he was the Coalbrookdale company's agent.

This group of capitalists was destined to become one of the most powerful in Cornwall, grasping at the new opportunities in the 1790s as the monopoly of Watt came to its close, and building a commercial empire that was to stretch to South Wales, where the Foxes owned

46

extensive collieries and iron mines. In 1792 they leased Neath Abbey
ironworks at Cwm Felin which included a foundry and copper-rolling
mills and so began an enterprise that was to have few equals anywhere
in the south-west of England. From their collieries and their blast-
furnaces they shipped coal and pig-iron over Welsh tramroads
through their port of Portreath and then over Cornish tramroads to
their foundry at Perran and in return shipped copper-ore over the
same routes to their smelters in Swansea. Both companies appear to
have been operated as a single enterprise, though at first most of the
advanced work was concentrated at Neath, first under Peter Price and
then under his son, Joseph Tregelles Price (1784–1854), who later
became a founding member of the Peace Society and whose humani-
tarian interests are perpetuated on a plaque on the wall of his
manager's house at the foundry at Neath Abbey. Only some of the
walls of the latter have survived, but the remains at Perran are
impressive, and should not be destroyed.

A first glance will show the ideal nature of its site. There was an
abundance of water coming down from Kennal Vale to work the
wheels and machinery, and the tidal inlet of the Fal gave access to the
sea. Though the creek was only navigable for vessels of shallow
draught, the company possessed its own barges which carried heavy
engine-parts down to the wharf at Restronguet Creek, where a 25 ton
crane lifted them on to ocean-going vessels. There is some evidence
that boilers were even floated down the river. By 1860, so great had
been the volume of work, the works were extended to cover an area
of 6 acres and employed 400 men; 9 engines were built for the Real
del Monte silver mines in Mexico, 3 for the Burra Burra mines in
South Australia and others for Spain and South America. Other fine
engines turned out by the foundry in the prime of its life were: in
1851 a 30in built for the Great Exhibition and later worked at Wheal
Cupid; in 1865 a 72in steam-cylinder and a 144in air-cylinder for the
Ebbw Vale Steel & Iron Company, the largest beam blowing-engine
ever built in Great Britain (the scale drawings can be seen at the
Cornish Engine Preservation Society's Museum at Holman's, Cam-

borne); in 1869 two 85in engines, one for Dolcoath near Camborne and the other for the Cat Hole Mine near Mold in North Wales; in 1870 another 85in for the Great Fron Fwnog Mine, also near Mold; in 1872 a 100in (11ft × 10ft) pumping engine for the Harris Navigation Colliery, Quaker's Yard, South Wales; and one of the three 84in and 144in Haarlem compounds for draining the Haarlem Meer in Holland. There is a disused Perran Foundry beam engine of 1878 at the Hodbarrow Iron Mine near Millom, Cumberland, probably now the only one in the world.

Unlike Harveys of Hayle, the company did not develop any other large-scale exports to offset the depression in mining and consequently had to shut down in 1879, its rivals buying the best of its machinery and its stocks of pig-iron, while the premises subsequently passed to the milling firm of Edwards Brothers (Perranarworthal) Ltd, who owned them until recently. The buildings are still in extremely good condition, impressive in size with their enormous beams and roof timbers and colourful with their red tiles. The smiths' shop and the loam shop, now marked only by their walls, are vast and spacious, as is the grass-covered cylinder casting-pit. The scale of the double-furnace chimneys with their brick bases is immense. Two cast-iron pumps are used as beam supports while over former gateways two cast-iron arches proclaim the legend 'Perran Foundry 1791'. Near the expansive courtyard and spanning the stream is a bridge, cast in one solid piece of iron, reputed to be the very last piece of work turned out by the foundry in 1879. The present owners possess several etchings of the foundry and complete plans can be found in the County Record Office at Truro.

Within the building is evidence of another activity of archaeological interest that deserves mention. When Edwards Brothers bought the property they combined milling with the buying of cloth, carding and dyeing it and selling it to local tailors, this enterprise only coming to an end when they exported it to South Wales and lost money. One room in the foundry still contains the trestles and tables on which the cloth was rolled.

Close to Perran Wharf and just outside Devoran on the main Truro to Falmouth road, lies the main building of what was once Basset's Foundry, an old-established concern that specialised in general and marine work, as it does today under the ownership of W. Visick & Sons who have operated it since 1893. None of the original machinery survives but the site is well worth visiting on account of the three magnificent waterwheels that once drove the machinery. One is undershot and the other two overshot, and they provide a fine illustration of the Cornish genius for damming an existing small stream to create a powerful head of water.

Only the buildings remain too of the once-powerful St Austell Foundry, now in the occupation of Harvey & Co Ltd, with the original inscription 'St. Austle Foundry 1849' still to be clearly seen over a doorway. It seems, however, to have been in existence before 1816, although it does not appear to have been building complete engines until about 1850 when, under the management of the Hodge family from Chacewater, it shipped one engine to Australia. Other engines known to have been built included: in 1851 two 50in for Chypraze Consols in the parish of St Enoder and for Wheal Uny; in 1852 four 70in for South Crenver, Wheal Tristram, Great Hewas and East Polgooth; an 80in for Wheal Mary Ann at Menheniot; a 24in pumping and stamping engine for Wheal Buller at St Just; and a 40in pumping engine for Boscean Mine, also at St Just.

When John Hodge died in 1855 the foundry was bought by William West, the great engineer at Fowey Consols, who seven years earlier had established his own foundry at St Blazey by the side of the Par canal. Its buildings, now used by builders' merchants, where repair and maintenance work was done for the mines around and several complete engines built, can still be seen: in 1849 a 30in for West Par Consols; in 1865 a 70in for the Rhymney Iron Company of South Wales; and two 80in engines, one for the Trewetha Mine near Liskeard and the other for Old Shepherds United. This foundry made cast-iron road bridges across the new railway from Par to Newquay, and five, dated 1873, are still in use in the Roche district.

As befitted a widely dispersed industrial and farming people, Cornwall possessed a multitude of other foundries, most of them rather small but efficient. Of these little trace survives: Calstock Tamar Ironworks, Wadebridge, Truro, Menheniot, Penryn, Saltash, St Agnes, Helston, Trevaunance, Launceston, Stithians and even Marazion. They were generally iron and brass foundries, engaged in the repair of engine-parts and agricultural tools, though the Wade-bridge foundry of Oatey & Martyn built several engines up to 40in and was in existence until as recently as 1945. Occasionally one meets with a foundry tucked away in the most unlikely of places, like the Battery Rolling Mills at St Erth, which manufactured Cornish shovels, jumpers, pitch-forks, axes, etc, and now serves as a piggery. Even the more famous foundries that served the entire mining area of Redruth have disappeared. Tuckingmill Foundry, established in 1833 by W. Vivian, was engaged in building engines by 1852 and was associated with the Roseworthy Hammer Mills between Camborne and Connor Downs established about 1790 by Joseph Vivian & Company and working until 1939. The Basset Foundry, established by F. Bartle & Company in 1860, was at Carn Brea. The Redruth Foundry, in existence before 1829 and under the management of James Carnell of Perran Foundry after 1859, built complete engines, while the Redruth Hammer Mills Foundry kept going until 1900. But of this group only one has lasted until the present day, the Tolgus Foundry, owned by the Sara family since April 1860.

Lying in the seclusion of a wooded hollow off the bypass road (A30) from Redruth to Truro this foundry will be completely missed by the passing motorist unless he sees its waterwheels turning as if in defiance of the technology of today, for it bears all the characteristics of an age that has long since vanished. Once known as Town Mills, it has manufactured an impressive range of articles for the local mining population: stamp-cams; stamp-heads; grid-irons for china-clay drys; weights and measures; manhole covers; Cornish ovens; and drills, one of which won a Royal Polytechnic Society award in 1885 and one of which the family still possesses. The roof timbers in the main shop are identical with those tremendous beams of wood that rose and fell in the pump-shafts of the mines. The equipment includes a face-plate and two early nineteenth-century lathes, one of which was purchased from Perran Wharf, and the remarkable thing is that they and the forges are powered, as they always were, by waterwheels. The foundry was built on to an older corn mill, whose grindstones were turned by a wheel, still there, that in turn was powered by a stream which at flood-time filled a pond whose waters were then controlled by a sluice-gate. Though the pond is now overgrown with weeds and shrubs, there is always sufficient water to move the other two wheels that drive the machinery in the foundry; and in Cornwall water-power is never handicapped by the disadvantages of droughts in summer and ice in winter as in other parts of the country. The larger of the two wheels, 30ft diameter, was cast by the Sara family in the foundry itself and drives the fan for the main furnace that is used for the smelting of the iron. The smaller wheel is 15ft diameter, overshot like the other, and drives all the machinery in the machine shop by a complicated system of belts and pulleys that seems antiquated but is admittedly economical, the costs being practically negligible.

Two other foundries are still in operation, having weathered the changing storms and depressions by adapting themselves to new conditions. Though they are not strictly 'archaeological', yet they contain much of archaeological interest. The Charlestown Foundry, just above the harbour built by Charles Rashleigh of Menabilly and now under the management of English China Clays, was established by J. & R. Michell in 1827 and then in 1835 was taken over by John Thomas of Redruth who formed the Charlestown Foundry & Ironworks Co in 1845. By the 1850s it was producing complete engines with 50in cylinders and in 1853 built a 70in for Mounts Bay Consols, afterwards specialising in boilers, bridges and general ironwork, though in 1911 it achieved the distinction of casting the last pumping-engine to be made in Cornwall, a 36in for North Goonbarrow Clay Works. The foundry still possesses in excellent working trim its

original 30ft pitch-back waterwheel, of a special type known as the
'Charlestown wheel', erected in 1852 for driving the forge-hammers
and other machinery, and now employed in pumping water and
generating a secondary supply of electricity. There is also a fine
specimen of a face-plate that was used for the turning of cylinders and
bobs, and for boring them. The original boiler-house is still in use,
complete with the bosses of iron that strengthened the walls and the
fluted cast-iron pillars that supported the roof, though these have
been bricked in now, the first foundry having no surrounding walls.
One of the columns, however, has been preserved as an example of
early casting. Running the entire length of the pattern-shop are
enormous timbers and trusses that were once the standard pump-rods
from some neighbouring mine. The original chimneys for the furnaces where the process of fagoting (fusing of scrap metal) of iron
was carried out are still there, as well as the house of the caretaker,
a conspicuous feature of most Cornish foundries.

The other foundry still in production is that of Holman Bros of
Camborne, world-famous for rock-drills and air-compressors today
and founded in 1801 by Nicholas Holman at Pool, where it was then
known as the Cornwall Boiler Works, specialising in general mining-
machinery, boiler making and beam engines. One of its best was the
80in built in 1909 for Phoenix United on Caradon Moor, though the
cylinder indeed had to be cast and bored in a Lancashire foundry. In
1834 Nicholas Holman jr left Camborne and erected another foundry
in the Tregeseal valley on the outskirts of St Just to cater for the
needs of the mines that had developed to a high degree of concentration in one of the most isolated regions of the county. Five years
later Holman opened another foundry in Penzance with the main
object of specialising in marine work and in 1880 their dry-dock was
constructed which today can accommodate vessels up to 700 tons and
is one of the busiest of its kind anywhere in the west country.
Inevitably, as the mines declined in West Penwith and the miners
took themselves off to America, South Africa and Australia, the
volume of work at the St Just foundry declined too, though it

Page 53 (above) *East Cornwall Minerals Railway showing engine shed and water tower at the incline station site near Calstock Consols;* (below) *waterwheel and balance box at Wheal Martyn clay works showing flat rod driving last Cornish 'lift', ie water-operated beam engine. See photograph overleaf*

Page 54 (above) *Wheal Martyn Cornish 'lift'. The flat rod pushes and pulls the 'bob' which operates the clay slurry pump. At the time the photograph was taken the pump rod had been taken out for repair;* (below) *trainload of De Lank granite destined for docks at Hartlepool in 1910 on the LSWR at Wenford*

was not until the early months of 1968 that the decision to close it down completely was finally taken. It was demolished later that year.

The class of work undertaken at St Just was of a high standard and wide range, serving many interests and demands, both in and out of the home. In 1854 the undertaking comprised a foundry, hammer mills, boiler works and several machine shops, all worked by water-wheels; its power-hammers were of the tilting type, driven by a beam engine. Several complete engines came from the foundry: in 1852 a 28in for Penzance Consols; in 1853 a 24in stamps-engine for the local Boscean Mine; and in 1860 a 17in horizontal engine for the Ovens Diggings in Australia. But the firm also cast Cornish boilers and installed them in many parts of the country; for instance in 1834 it supplied boilers to the Portsmouth Farrington Waterworks. It designed and built pumps and pumping machinery, waterwheels, pithead gear and cages (one very special order was for the Sudan Goldfields Mining Company) and tram-waggons of the universal swivelling type. It catered for a wide range of ironwork, without which domestic and mining development in the district would have been considerably retarded, producing items as dissimilar as the main gates to the entrance to St Just church; the Gear Rock beacon on the extremity of a reef off Penzance in Mounts Bay; a coal-gas plant at St Just; Cornish 'slabs'—iron ovens that revolutionised the cooking in the miner's home and became a welcome amenity in lighthouses all around the coasts; capstans and heating stoves for the fishing industry; road signs; lifting cultivators and iron ploughs; and water-heating systems for schools and halls. But the inhabitants of Penzance may see the work of this foundry in the valley by looking at the iron railings, of a simple yet distinctive design, that it rolled out for edging the town's long Promenade in 1865 and The Terrace in Market Jew Street about a decade later; the standards that carried gas lamps and which have now been adapted to carry electric lamps, several of them bearing the maker's name; and the gratings, hydrant covers and manhole covers that appear in every street. This foundry possessed

D

a very early planing machine made by Joseph Whitworth of Manchester in 1839. It was recently removed to a private collection in Newdigate, Surrey, after a working life of 129 years for Cornish industry.

CHAPTER FOUR

Tin Mines and Tin Smelters

TIN MINES

THE main tin areas of Cornwall fall into well-defined districts which are distinct and separate from those of the copper regions around Redruth and Camborne and East Cornwall. With the exception of St Austell and St Agnes, the main centres were concentrated west of Truro, around Wendron, Breage, St Ives and, above all, in the extreme west around St Just-in-Penwith, where the mining of tin had been in operation since the seventeenth century and was responsible for the designation of Penzance as a coinage town in 1663. From the sea and from the beaches it is not difficult to comprehend why this should be so, for the land structure was favourable to lode mining, the ground being excavated to a depth of forty fathoms or so by adits driven in from the cliffs, many of which can still be detected today. Moreover, the whole district of St Just, in spite of its lack of rivers and streams, was blessed with very considerable winter rains that made it a veritable reservoir of water-power as may be seen from the in-numerable wheel pits that lie scattered over the landscape. And, of course, St Just is one of the two places in Cornwall that still carries on this ancient industry, for it is the home of the successful Geevor Tin Mine whose engineers are now exploring the lodes beneath Levant Mine, following the unwatering after the sea's long domination there.

The St Just Area

The best way to examine this intensively mineralised zone is to approach it from Penzance and then to work from south to north after a visit to the lone splendour of Ding Dong (189/434345) that dominates the skyline for miles around with its massive engine house, bricked-in shaft and superb cylinder-mounting. Compared to the wild moorland here, over which the local hounds safely hunt the fox, so free is it of all other evidence of its industrial past, the path to St Just is littered with remains. Down by the beach at Nanjizal or Mill Bay are the remains of a stamp mill and a wheel pit, while a large cave nearby is undoubtedly manmade, since the tin lode outcrops here. In Nanjulian Valley at the seaward end are extensive tin-dressing floors, two wheel pits, part of the wheel of what is known as Pod Mill, together with evidence of early cliff mining on the south side of the valley. In Bosworlas Valley near Jasmine Cottage are the remains of still more stamps that were once a part of Bosworlas Mine, now almost completely forgotten but for the names of the neighbouring fields, Stamps and Leat Meadow. At Trevegean, a place of small-scale mining in the 1870s, lie a couple of buddles not far from a field called Engine Field, the only record now of past activity, hopes and disappointments. The entire length of these cliffs is pitted with the scars of endeavours that sustained life in these valleys. In the 1840s, thirty-five men erected a waterwheel 20ft diameter and dressed their ore at Carn Leskys, where today there are only shafts and patches of level ground. At Letcha they are only remembered by Whim Field, and above Progo by workings in the cliff face, where once stood Hermon Mine, called Wheal Ermine by local people. Cot Valley teems with interest, for its sides were extensively dug out for stream tin and its floor still shows evidence of at least three stamps, a small smelter and the lines of two buddles, remains of an enterprise in which Pascoe Grenfell may have been concerned, since he owned the land. In the same valley, now converted into holiday accommodation, are the Killinack Manor Mills—a pair of grist mills, according to the 1890 *Tithe Book*, whose machinery was removed in the 1940s and placed in Helston Museum.

The town of St Just reflects the quality and character of the occupations that have given life to its people for centuries. There are

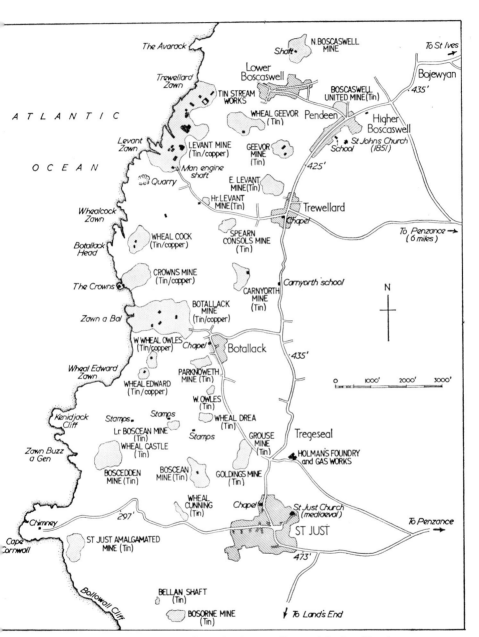

The metal mines between the Atlantic coastline and St Just/Pendeen

terraces upon terraces of sturdy granite cottages, often built by the miners themselves with their own hands and in their own time, when work at the mines was plentiful; the more elegant houses of the managers and the superintendents; and their chapels and the church, the latter graced by iron gates that were cast in Holman's Foundry in Tregeseal Valley. The spacious square, flanked by hostelries of varying antiquity, has always been known as Bank Square and there a butcher's shop, which was once the Capital & Counties Bank as the name incised in the granite lintel above the window shows, is an important survival of the days when the financing of the mines depended so much on the credit of the country banks. A short distance away near the Clock Tower, where a store now stands, is the site of the former Post Office where, in the terrible days of depression, it was possible to buy a through ticket to Johannesburg or to Hancock in Michigan. Of greater antiquity is the spacious medieval theatre-in-the-round, the Plain-an-Gwary, now conspicuous for its disarray of granite blocks holed with the marks of miners' drills when they were the target of drilling contests. Further down the road are two buildings of industrial significance: the Lafrowda Club with its classical front of columns and pediment where the St Just Literary & Scientific Society was born in 1842 as an attempt to bring sweetness and light to an otherwise drab mining town; and the Working Men's Club, built after the disaster at the Levant Mine in 1919, but founded in 1895.

At St Just one is continually coming across the unexpected. To the west of the town, best approached by a footpath across the fields, is Kelynack, a hamlet of no special significance perhaps were it not for the fact that it is the place of the last surviving blacksmith's shop, owned and worked by Mr Jim Williams who can trace its history back to the 1760s, when it was opened by one Peter James to serve the local farmers. In the ground outside the main shop is the wheel-wright's contrivance for binding iron rims on to the wheels of carts—a flat piece of granite with a circular hole cut in the middle in which the box of the wheel was placed. Inside the smithy can be found a whole range of tools and equipment of a previous age: a lathe made locally; tools for cutting local threads in the days long before standardisation (there was a St Just thread and a St Buryan thread although the two places are no more than 6 miles apart); an anvil on a granite base; a granite trough in which 'slack' was mixed with water for banking the fire; and wooden wall drills. This unpretentious granite structure is the last of at least twelve shops between Sennen and Trewellard that served the smaller mines and farms in the district, repairing their equipment, sharpening their drills and even making disc harrows, still known locally as 'tormentors' as they were in the days when they first made their appearance in the walled fields around St Just.

From Kelynack (189/371300) it is best to work northwards along the coast towards Cape Cornwall, taking on the way the counthouse of Bosorne Mine and the ruined surface buildings and tall stack of St Just United and Bolowal Mines. Not much now exists, on the ground, of Cape Cornwall Mine out on the headland, with its superb views of the Atlantic though its miners had little time for that. Yet what little remains is of spectacular interest. Dominating the scene is the single stack of the mine and the twisting line of masonry flues running the length of the towering cliff, so constructed as to give the maximum draught, while below on a level strip of ground stands the counthouse. On the north-east side of the cape is a building that was once a blacksmith's shop and a leat that ran across the cape from the direction of Wheal Call just past St Helen's Chapel. The latter mine, also known as Boswedden, was worked almost on the beach down in Nancherrow Valley and can still be, to some extent, identified by a dwelling-house known as Wheal Call, which was the counthouse, by several leats traversing the cliff and by the remains of a tremendous wheel pit in which must have turned a waterwheel that had a diameter of about 65ft, second only to the 72ft giant at Laxey in the Isle of Man. Wheal Castle nearby can likewise be identified by a wheel pit of large dimensions, heaps of spoil, ruined walls, a small chimney and depressions in the ground that marked the path of a tramroad.

So often has the ground been worked over and setts divided and subdivided by generation after generation of miners and adventurers that it now resembles a honeycomb. The Kenidjack Valley from south to north is a cultural landscape of the many past occupations and activities and technologies that maintained life in this area for many years: a dwelling-house that once sheltered the poor; a grist mill and the remains of the miller's cottage; a large dam for retaining water; the tall stack of a calciner; several stamp-mills, one of which houses an 8ft waterwheel turning in a 10ft pit that pumped water from an adit that emerges from Carn Praunter up to Kenidjack Farm and Truthwall; two quarries; iron rings driven into the face of the cliff below for tying up the miners' fishing boats; the shell of an explosive store; and the remains of a tramway crossing the road just west of Kenidjack hamlet that led to the quarry. Further up the valley are more stamps and the counthouse and stack of Boscean Mine.

Above Kenidjack the heavily industrialised belt becomes deeper and denser as evidenced by tumbled-down miners' cottages now used for farm outhouses; the engine house of Wheal Drea; and just south of Truthwall (189/368325) the last vestiges of Wheal Boys. At Truthwall itself looms the engine house and counthouse of one of the most celebrated, and tragic, mines in the area, Wheal Owles. In the 1850s eight steam engines were working here to keep the mine free of water, but in 1893 the water won and drowned twenty-nine miners, whose bodies were never recovered, and so heavy was the sense of doom at the failure to give them a Christian burial that the mine and its victims were abandoned. Part of the Wheal Owles sett was Wheal Edward, to be distinguished now by the remains of its two engine houses. At Tregeseal, opposite the bridge at the bottom of the steep hill that turns up in the direction of Holman's Foundry, is a shop that was once a counthouse and then a tollhouse. A little further up the valley is a grist mill with part of the millstone in a garden; at Bosvargas is another mill that has been used for both grinding corn and stamping tin ore, with the leat still visible as it crosses the road;

and then very suddenly there appears the vast complex of the two greatest mines in West Cornwall, Botallack and Levant. But, before these are described in detail, mention must be made of several others that defy any attempt to place them in a neat geographical pattern: Balleswidden Mine that produced 11,830 tons of black tin between 1837 and 1873, lying athwart the A3071 Penzance road 1 mile east of St Just, and at one time only second to Wheal Vor when it cut rich in 1841 with five engines and 634 people working there; the engine house of Boscaswell Down Mine, to the end of which a dwelling-house has been built and whose shaft has recently been recapped in preparation for a new working by Geevor Tin Mines; on the cliffs near the lighthouse the counthouse of Pendeen Consols, whose levels reached out beneath the sea; and the two engine houses of Wheal Hearle on the exposed moor close to Pendeen crossroads on the Pendeen–Penzance road.

For the industrial archaeologist who wishes to discover and re-construct for himself all the processes for the recovery and winning of tin and copper, no starting point could be better than Botallack Mine at 189/364333, for at least three separate workings of the ground can be discerned in an area that is compact and neat in its remains. Botallack was renowned in its day, and still is, for its two magnificent engine houses perched almost precariously on the edge of the cliff, which were the object of so much awe that they were visited by royalty and so have become more generally known as the Crowns section. The larger of the two was built probably before 1816 and even now remains a remarkable example of precision engineering as well as a tribute to the ingenuity and skill in both civil and mechanical engineering of its Cornish constructors. It is unusual in that the stack is built inside the house, no doubt on account of the exceptionally narrow and confined ground of the promontory on which it stands; it is remarkable in that the massive granite blocks used for the bob-wall and for most of the whim engine house had all to be lowered over the cliff before being placed in position, the restricted place allowing very little margin of error. Though the engine was small, a 30in,

built by Harveys of Hayle in 1823, drawing, in 1839, 150 fathoms
with 7in pumps and raising only 15 to 27 gallons of water every
minute, nevertheless the engine parts, cylinders and cylinder
mounting too had to be hauled and manhandled down the steep
cliff.

The rocky promontory on which the house stands has a conspicuous deep cut on its seaward side, and this is evidence of an even
earlier working for copper before the above engine house was erected.
What its form was can be seen from some of the first etchings made
of Botallack in the latter years of the eighteenth century (there is one
in the Penzance Library in the Morrab Gardens, Penzance), which
show the ore being hoisted in buckets up this cut by means of a
windlass.

The smaller engine house a little higher up the cliff was built about
1858–9 when the mine was running out of copper and on the point
of producing more tin, so that it was found necessary to sink another
shaft, a diagonal one called the Boscawen. It was to work the hoist,
both for the ore and the men, that this second engine house was
built. It will be noticed that it apparently has no stack, but traces of
a flue can be followed from the house and up the side of the cliff by
an abandoned wall terminating in what was the base of the stack. The
reason for placing the stack so far from the house, of course, was to
increase the draught for the boiler furnace. From 1860 until 1895,
when it was abandoned, this section of Botallack sold £829,664 of
black tin, £220,707 of copper ore and £6,481 of arsenic. Yet nothing
now remains of its surface buildings (even though in 1883 it boasted
4 pumping engines, 2 sets of steam-stamps and 3 whim-engines)
except the engine house, a short section of walling, some iron eye-
bolts driven into the rock face, the counthouse and water tanks in
front of it, and towards the village a line of low-slung buildings, now
holiday flats, which housed the Penzance Mining School when it took
over a deserted Botallack in the 1890s for the practical instruction of
its students.

The complicated network of ruined buildings that face the visitor at the top of the cliff after leaving the counthouse and before descending to the Crowns section belongs to the year 1906, when a new company decided to reopen the old workings, but the result was disastrous for the venture only lasted until 1914. In a sense this complex is an illustration of the tragic and wasteful side of Cornish tin mining when it was already clearly apparent that, for the industry to survive, it would have to cut its enormous losses in the face of continuing and increasing competition from Bolivia and Malaya. The surface buildings are on an unnecessary and lavish scale, more money having been spent above than below 'grass'. Yet here can be traced all the complicated processes for the winning and treating of the tin, making it a veritable working laboratory for the industrial archaeologist: three concrete water tanks, filled from the mine and then used for the processes of riffling and buddling; the exceptionally massive engine house and stack; and the buildings that housed the compressors, in effect now looking very much like a ruined abbey. The stack was hardly ever used, as the elaborately built masonry flues show, since in 1906 the company did not use steam engines, but four expensive gas-engines to work the pumps, and then after 1911 electric pumps, the current being brought from the new power station at Hayle. For ornateness there is nothing to compare with the room that contained the electric generator, for it rested on a floor of Italian mosaic, later it is said removed to a private house in Heamoor. The railed-off entrance to Allen's vertical shaft hides the story of three years of continual excavation that consumed a colossal amount of capital. The dressing-floors are some of the most beautifully constructed anywhere in Cornwall and the buddles are miracles of precision. But without a doubt the most impressive group of buildings are the calciners and the elaborate system of flues and chambers leading to the main stack (where the black tin was roasted to drive off the arsenic and sulphur) looking like a line of silver-lead smelters in the Arizona desert, or the beehive tombs of an ancient civilisation in the Aegean. Rumour has it that no tin was ever brought to the surface before the depression hit it in 1914, when the mine and its

machinery were advertised for sale, and it remains as a sad commentary on the decline of Cornwall's staple industry. Yet, sophisti-
cated as it is, the quality of the building will not bear comparison with
that of the engine houses of 1816 and 1859, cut and dressed granite
giving way to random rubble, as the Cornish mason calls it, and
concrete.

Levant Mine, almost next door at 189/360340, is equally complex,
but much more difficult to reconstruct because of the ruinous state of
all the surface buildings. Like Botallack it was first worked for copper
in the 1820s, and it is to this period that what is probably the oldest
engine extant in Cornwall belongs. It is a beam whim-engine, double-
acting 24in cylinder with a 4ft stroke, built by Harveys of Hayle in
1840 and rebuilt by Hocking & Loam in 1862 with a new cylinder and
valve-gear after an accident which caused the flywheel to be thrown
through the roof. This engine worked continuously for ninety years
at its task of raising ore and only stopped when Levant was abandoned
in 1930. It is *in situ* with its machinery intact in the original and
unusually squat house overlooking the sea and the fearful zawn
(chasm) below. It is now under the care of the National Trust,
through the efforts of the Cornish Engine Preservation Society since
1935. Copper was taken out as late as 1910, making Levant the last
of the truly great copper mines to survive.

The mine was also being continuously worked for tin in the nineteenth century when the adventurers were Daubuz and Batten of
Trereife smelting house, and was subject to successive booms and
slumps that afflicted tin, declining through the 1860s and then being
abandoned in 1871 because of disputes between the adventurers and
the smelters: the miners contended with justification that they worked
too close to the sea. In 1871 a new company took over the dilapidated
workings, an operation that cost £17,500 before a single ton of tin was
raised, and just managed to survive the acute depression of 1878.
How disastrous the reopening was may be gathered from the fact
that in 1898 its profits were a mere £146, although it had sold £10,000
of black tin. Then Francis Oats, who had been a successful director

of de Beer Diamonds Consolidated and was a St Just man, returned from South Africa and started the Basset Mines Group to rework Levant on a lavish scale, thereby unwittingly contributing to a feeling of false prosperity, though making work available to many who otherwise would have found themselves in the poor house. Perhaps the North Levant engine house with its magnificently cut ore chutes and steps on the right-hand side of the road into Levant is his best memorial (apart from the house he built, now Cape Cornwall Hotel), though visible evidence of his troubles are not at all difficult to find, such as the half-completed engine house and the lines of a shaft he never sank. His aims were high and he was determined to do the best for the workers where others had failed. For instance there used to be a beautifully shaped granite staircase, perhaps unique in Cornwall, that would have graced a church tower; the miners used this to bring them from the main shaft to the 'dry', where baths were sunk into the floor which can still be seen, though the 'dry' has long since lost its roof and walls. Men walked down these winding stairs to the topmost rod of the man-engine that would take them down to the levels and did so for many years until October 1919 when it collapsed, killed thirty-one miners and injured nineteen others. Nothing now remains to remind one of that terrible disaster except the ruined engine-house stack built in 1893 to work the horizontal engine and air-compressors, and the building nearby known as the Death House, where the human remains were assembled in some kind of order for burial.

The tragedy seemed part of the nature of the mine's difficult history, for its problems were unique. The best ores were to be found further and further west of the main shafts, and so the stopes were being worked $1\frac{1}{2}$ miles beneath the sea, where ventilation was always a major problem. Though Levant was a relatively dry mine, the men were always troubled by their unnatural proximity to the sea and so drifted away. Those who stayed lived in the gloom of the 1919 disaster and, when the main shaft was closed, climbed down the precipitous and nauseating zawn towards the boiling surf to enter the mine from the adits below. Everywhere today is a desolation that manifests the sad end of a once mighty enterprise: fallen crushers and ruined stamp-mills; buddles of finely cut masonry that would not disgrace a Norman font in a cathedral; elaborate calciners, settling tanks and reddened slime pits; a complicated network of roads, strewn with occasional kibbles and twisted ironwork; the piles of granite blocks that once housed brand-new electric compressors, and others that formed a new mill of two heads of Nissen stamps and five heads of California stamps, erected in 1921 in a vain attempt to stave off the coming disaster. By March 1929, in spite of its mammoth output of tin and copper, it still owed the adventurers and creditors £29,000 and shares slumped disastrously from 10s to 6d (50p to 2½p). Perhaps the saddest commentary of all are the ruins of the arsenic works, completed in 1918 to keep the mine solvent; now it is an impossible devastation of rubble that was once furnaces and flues, scraped clean every two months by men who wore special clothing, were dosed with medicine and were only paid a wage of 5s 6d (27½p) per shift for this dangerous and filthy work. But even this enterprise was too late, never cleared its costs and, with the war coming to an end, collapsed.

Pendeen to St Ives

East of Pendeen and towards St Ives begins the second tin-belt. If it be approached from Pendeen along the main road towards Morvah which takes in some of the most spectacular sea and cliff landscape, north of Morvah and hidden from the road will be found the remains of Morvah Consols and at 189/438382 part of the engine house of the Gurnard's Head Mine, exposed to the full force of the Atlantic gales; while at the edge of the road near Zennor stand the pumping and winding engine houses of Carn Galver Mine, otherwise known as Rosemergy Mine, from which down to the cliffs may be traced many wheel pits. Nearer to St Ives itself, on the slopes of Rosewall Hill, are the remains of the Rosewall and Ransom United Mines, both closed in 1876, and to the south those of Tyringham Consols, active for a few

years only in the 1860s. Of the richest mine in the entire area, St Ives
Consols, south-east of St Ives near the junction of the B3306 and
B3311 Penzance roads at 189/505398, little can now be found. Famous
for its great carbona and a prodigious producer of black tin—no less
than 16,400 tons between 1827 and 1892—its workings were cavernous
in the extreme, requiring a forest of timbers that caught fire in 1844.
Now its only remains are a few granite blocks, a wheel pit or two and
the counthouse, now occupied by the vehicles of a haulage contractor. Its chief adventurer, James Halse, was luckier, for he founded
a village nearby in the 1830s for his workers who promptly voted for
him on every occasion when he wanted to be returned to Parliament,
and today it is still called Halsetown.

Southwards from Halsetown along the main Penzance road at the
hamlet of Cripple's Ease is a mine in a good state of preservation in
sharp contrast to the rubble of what was once Wheal Reeth, which
was so rich that it had its own smelter and between 1800 and 1835
returned a profit of £200,000. Giew, sometimes known as South
Providence, the Billa Mine and Reeth Consols, on the slopes of Trink
Hill at 189/501369 in the parish of Nancledra, is so compact that it
is perhaps the first mine that should be visited by the student who
wishes to view the cultural landscape of tin mining. An extension of
the older Providence sett that stretched along the Hayle–St Ives road
from the coast inland towards and beyond Knill's Monument, whose
mound of tailings are a golden reminder of 9,700 tons of black tin won
between 1835 and 1862, Giew was the very last of the tin mines to
cease working in 1923, bringing this ancient industry to a complete
stop for the first time in its history. Its engine house is a gem of its
kind, with window frames of iron and the inscription 's.p. 1871'
incised on a lintel: but the stack may be a false one, or perhaps was
never used, though there is some record of steam-stamps being
employed. Local miners remember that the hoist was worked by
electricity, the power being brought from Hayle on pylons, some of
which can still be seen, though sawn down almost to the level of the
ground. The main shaft is exposed and most unsafe, and near it are

the concrete walls of three forges and immense pits in which turned the flywheels of the compressors.

The ore was trammed across the present main B3311 road to Penzance near the present Giew House, formerly the counthouse and office, in 1 ton trams along a short embankment that is still clearly visible, and down the natural slope of the ground. From here it is not at all difficult to follow the sequence of processes: the remains of a crushing shed; the water tanks, still full of water; a wall which carried the tramroad; the level dressing-floors where the stamps were bolted to the masonry, though only a little of the immense wooden pillars remain, the rest having been cut away for kindling wood; a pile of rounded stones and boulders that were used for crushing; the buddling sheds; and finally the calciner and its stack, both in excellent condition.

Once again these relics are a reminder of the difficulties of this mine, for the veins corkscrewed and the ventilation was bad. Survivors of the depression of the 1920s recall with bitterness the less lucky ones who finished their early days in the local 'bone-yard' while they themselves were forced to accept a cut in wages to keep the mine afloat or find work at the local china-clay pit. So, when in 1923 the hard decision was made to close the mine, all the machinery had to be sold to placate the creditors. The same fate fell to Wheal Sisters (Margaret, Mary and Kitty) in the same parish along the valley between Trink Hill and Trencrom Hill, but somehow a set of stamps survived and these can be seen among a tangle of brambles and undergrowth; there are also two splendid engine houses as well, worthy of a group of mines that produced 12,950 tons of black tin and 10,700 tons of copper ore from 1825 to 1900.

Mounts Bay

Along the shores of Mounts Bay runs an old tin-lode, not far from the site of the ancient port of Iktin in Marazion. It travels from Newlyn at the old West Tolvadden Mine beneath the sea to the

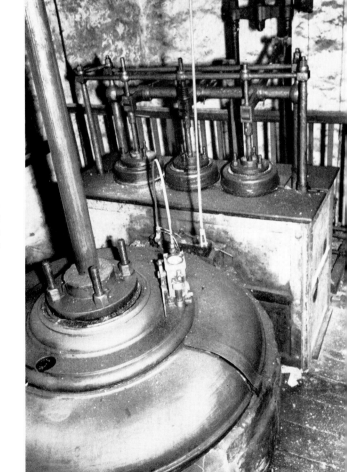

Page 71 (above) *Blondin at slip china-stone quarry at Goonvean; (right) cylinder cap, piston rod and valves of the last beam engine to work in Cornwall, at Greensplat china-clay works. The engine, possibly 140 years old, stopped on 22 February 1959*

Page 72   *Installation of 35ft waterwheel at Tregargus stone-grinding mills, St Stephen, in 1896. Built by Edward Bartle of Carn Brea Foundry*

rocks, where once stood the now almost forgotten Mexico Mine (189/500313 approx) and included the Wherry Mine almost at Newlyn. But the real paying lode begins at Marazion and extends eastwards between Tregonning Hill and Godolphin Hill in the direction of Porthleven. Resplendent among the many ruins of bygone adventures on the road to Goldsithney and St Hilary stand the magnificent engine house and stack of Tregurtha Downs Mine with a shorter calciner stack nearby. Of a most unusual height and design (there is only one other like it, that of the lead mine East Wheal Rose), it is said to be by a London architect who wanted it to resemble a Cornish chapel (plate p 18). It belongs to the last reworking between 1903 and 1914 under the name of Wheal Hampton, though the mine's history goes back to the middle of the eighteenth century when it ran into financial troubles because of its distance from the nearest smelter at Treloweth and the coinage town of Helston. The present house was built to take an 80in engine designed by Samuel Grose which had originally been made in 1854 at the Copperhouse Foundry, Hayle, for Wheal Alfred Consols, at a cost of over £3,000. It was then removed to Crenver and Wheal Abraham before coming to Tregurtha Down, so widespread was the migration of the Cornish engine. It is now preserved at South Crofty Mine at Pool, Camborne, in the care of the National Trust.

Further inland, near Relubbas, stands the engine house of the Tregembo Mine, a small affair that worked successfully and intermittently until 1888; and then 1 mile west of Godolphin Hill in the St Hilary area the two engine houses of Tindene Mine, that went out of production in 1892. In the saddle between Godolphin Hill and Tregonning Hill yet another engine house survives in this rich tin area, that of Great Work which, between 1832 and 1902, raised 6,256 tons of black tin. It is the last of three which survived until 1930, the whim being pulled down at the start of a reworking and the stamps-engine quite recently. At the foot of Tregonning Hill, close to the main road between Germoe and Ashton, lies a cluster of buildings, stacks and half of an engine house that belonged to one of the oldest

E

mines in West Cornwall, Wheal Grey, which was in production long before William Cookworthy discovered china clay near the same site about 1745. Further eastwards on Carleen Downs at 189/621302 is revealed a scene of utter desolation that was once the pride of the county and even the nation—Great Wheal Vor, a grim memorial to the folly of reopening old mines. From 1820 to 1845 the mine produced a profit of almost £200,000 and then, between 1850 and 1870 during the tedious period of unwatering and looking in vain for the errant ore, lost almost as much money so that every scrap of machinery and building had to be sold off. Nothing now remains of this town and mine that housed over 1,000 workers, several pumping engines, eight whims, a 36in engine that turned 88 heads of stamps, and a tramroad 1,200ft long from the main shaft to the stamps, except a few granite superstructures, traces of water tanks and heaps of spoil. The same fate has befallen Great Wheal Fortune at 189/628285, also on Carleen Downs in the valley leading down to the harbour of Porthleven. From 1855 to 1891 more than 3,000 tons of black tin came out of these gulches and shafts, now covered by a matting of red-berried cotoneaster; and it is now almost impossible to believe that these downs supported a working population of nearly 500 persons. Only a manager's house still stands (now a farm); vast incisions in the granite; and the faint traces of a tramroad and footpaths once laden with the weight of the ore-waggons. More substantial remains, however, are to be found at the two mines on which the adventurers concentrated after the failure of Wheal Vor. Scott's Mine at 189/622295 has a fine engine house, two buddles in sound condition, water tanks and part of a blacksmith's shop; while Wheal Metal at 189/629299 boasts a colossal engine house that should last for many years as a memorial of men's endeavours.

Helston to Wendron

Another string of tin mines, though less important and concentrated in a much smaller area, runs in a north-easterly direction from

Helston through the villages of Wendron and Porkellis along the B3297 road to Penryn. Though small in size and their output together rather less than that of any single mine in the St Just area, yet they are not without their archaeological charm and interest today, for much of the prosperity of Helston depended on their continuing output. Almost the entire area south of Wendron between the B3297 and A394 roads is occupied by the remnants of Trumpet Consols which, from 1854 to 1880, pulled up 4,510 tons of black tin; it included Wheal Dream and Wheal Ann and the engine house of the latter stands close to the B3297 road, half a mile south-west of Wendron. Due south of the village of Porkellis and north-west of Wendron are the surface workings and the engine house of Basset & Grylls Mine (named after two important landowners from Redruth and Helston), which, between 1852 and 1914, cleared 4,650 tons of black tin and was subject to several reworkings, the last being as recently as 1930. Other mines of interest on the way to Penryn are: near Carnebone the engine house of East Wheal Lovell (2,405 tons, 1859–91); on the same road the ivy-covered stacks and ruins of an engine house of Great Wheal Lovell; north of Porkellis on the slopes of Carnmenellis the engine house of the shallow Medlyn Moor Mine; and close to the main Falmouth road near Rame the single stack of the Bal Ding Mine at Retanna.

St Austell

In the china-clay districts around St Austell tin has also been found, though nothing like to the same extent as in West Cornwall. Yet it should be remembered that in the early days of the working of china clay, tin was worked at the same time and often in association with the clay, successes in the one sometimes offsetting failures in the other, producing a balanced economy that occurred nowhere else in Cornwall. Carclaze Mine is the best illustration of this dual role, an impressive pit 130ft deep and 5 acres in extent beside the north road of Tregonissey Lane End, said to have been producing tin in the days of Henry VI. Today it remains the only work we have comparable to the spectacular copper amphitheatres of strip mining in Montana, Utah and Arizona. Northwards on Hensbarrow Beacon, countless small tin mines flourished for a time, though their remains have long been buried under subsequent clay workings. Outstanding in this area were Great Beam Mine, very active in the 1820s but extinguished about 1872 and remarkable, as were all the mines around, on account of the immense amount of timber required because the shafts were sunk in decomposed granite; Charlestown United on the north side of the main road, inland from the harbour at Holmbush (6,660 tons, 1864–92) which, in the capable hands of John Taylor, cut very rich after 1819 and proved only second to Wheal Vor; and its successor along the same sett, Wheal Eliza (9,320 tons, 1864–92). Today, on the white landscape of booming clay, tin is of no account and no more than a memory, but yesterday St Austell's 'best friend' was Great Polgooth Mine, east of the village of Sticker. Now only the stump of an engine house reminds us that in 1741 it was one of the only three mines in Cornwall rich enough to afford a Newcomen atmospheric engine; that in 1797 it possessed 50 shafts and employed over 1,000 persons; that it had been to the fore in making use of an early 58in Boulton & Watt engine; and that John Taylor breathed new life into the old workings in 1820 with an impressive array of the latest machinery (South Polgooth, however, has an engine house and a calciner). Three other mines have contributed to the general tale of depression since about 1900: Ventonwyn and its stamps engine house and stack near the A39 road, sold up in 1907; Great Dowgas, now only a stack; and St Austell Consols with its ruined engine houses.

Other Outstanding Tin Mines

In several areas, of course, tin was mined in association with copper and, wherever this occurred, as for example around Illogan, Camborne, Gwennap, St Day, Gunnislake, and Kit Hill, such mines have been described in Chapter Two. There were, however, outstanding tin mines in predominantly copper areas such as Redruth–Chace-water. On the left-hand side of the road from Truro to Redruth immediately beyond Chacewater stands the impressive line of engine houses of Killifreth Mine (4,060 tons of black tin, 1859–1904) and on the right-hand side of the road the engine house of the equally redoubtable Wheal Busy. They tower above and dominate an industrial landscape that man has imposed on a natural landscape of remarkable beauty which stretches almost the whole of the way to Falmouth. Then, between the old Scorrier railway station and the Redruth bypass, rises the trinity of engine houses that mark the site of Wheal Peevor, a mine that in seventeen years of operation, 1872-89, produced 3,280 tons of metal. Nearer to Redruth, adjoining the southern boundary of East Carn Brea and close to the old incline of the former GWR Tresavean branch-line, is the ruined whim engine house of Wheal Uny (7,660 tons, 1853–93); and then, 5 miles to its south at Porkellis, that of Wheal Enys with part of its bob-wall bricked up as if someone thought of converting it into a dwelling-house. Finally, in the heart of Redruth itself and just above the present railway station, points skywards the striking stack of Ped'n-an-Drea Mine, stepped in great tiers, though now much reduced in height. As D. B. Barton remarks in his *The Cornish Beam Engine*:

> Originally this was no less than 140ft high, built almost entirely of killas but with granite for the rings dividing each section and with bricks used for the topmost four sections, now removed. In 1824 the masons and others 'celebrated the completion of its building by drinking a barrel of ale on its top.' The 70in engine (erected by Woolf) that this stack served worked only to 1827 and the structure thereafter became solely a landmark. By 1832 a ladder-way had been constructed in the bore and in June of that year, to celebrate the passing of the Reform Bill, tar-barrels were burned on its top and there was a firework display before a crowd of some 6,000.

Similarly, the areas of Porthtowan and St Agnes to the north, though fundamentally copper-producing, contain tin mines of considerable importance, as their ruins today testify in a land where sea and sky are hardly less spectacular than around St Just. The old mining town of St Agnes, near its brown moorland beacon, drew its

sustenance from some exceedingly rich producers in their time: West
Wheal Kitty (10,000 tons, 1881–1915) now marked by its engine
house and stack, closed 1941; Royal Polberro Consols, whose house
and stacks are the only record of tin that was so pure that it was taken
straight to the smelters; and Wheal Friendly, now reduced to one
engine house. East of St Agnes on the high plateau between Trevaunance Coombe and Trevellas Coombe lie the vast and complicated
remains of Penhalls Mine (3,610 tons, 1834–96) and Wheal Kitty
(9,510 tons, 1853–1918), which became a joint concern in 1907, closed
in 1919 and was reworked from 1926 to 1930: engine houses, dressing-
floors, mill, stamps, buddles and calciners. Finally, at the seaward end
of Trevellas Coombe, appear the engine house, two stacks and a few
crumbling walls that were once Blue Hills Mine and East Blue Hills
Mine, which together grossed 2,120 tons of black tin between 1858
and 1897.

TIN SMELTING AND THE COINAGE TOWNS

Harsh judgements have been passed on these sad reliques of Cornwall's great industrial history, particularly that they are crumbling
monuments to inefficiency, over-production and killing competition
from Malaya, Australia and Bolivia, which few adventurers heeded.
An examination of the physical remains alone is insufficient for
arriving at even an approximation of the truth, for it needs a searching
enquiry into the financial and business sides of the industry as
D. B. Barton has so ably made in his *A History of Tin Mining and
Tin Smelting in Cornwall*. Yet the industrial archaeologist can examine
on the ground two further aspects of the industry which will serve to
explain why considerable losses were made in the mining of tin and
handsome profits made in its smelting.

It will not have escaped the notice of even the most casual observer
that there are certain Cornish towns with a road called Coinagehall
Street. In every case this term is the sole surviving physical record of
a very distinctive feature of the tin industry which made it so different

from copper. Tin was a restricted and protected industry and had been since the time when King John regulated all aspects of tin mining under what was known as the Stannaries. Stannary Law gave the miner exemption from military service and market tolls, and permitted him to search for tin on unenclosed common land. In return, the tin he produced was taxed by the Crown—and after 1838 by the Duke of Cornwall—through a system of coinage, several towns being designated as coinage towns where, at a fixed time of the year, the blocks of tin were assayed and weighed by the officers of the Duchy of Cornwall under a complicated and elaborate code of rules and regulations in a coinage hall set aside for the purpose. The designated towns in Cornwall in medieval times were Bodmin, Lostwithiel, Liskeard, Truro and Helston but, as the tin-centre moved further west, Bodmin and Lostwithiel were abolished and Penzance created in their place. The system was wasteful and costly and, since the coinages were held only twice a year, blocks of tin tended to pile up in the streets of the coinage towns waiting the arrival of the duchy officers. Many mines, working on margins, could not afford this long wait and the rising costs of moving tin from the remote areas where it was worked. By 1833 it was clear that the coinage system was outmoded, especially since it took no account of the rate at which the price tended to fluctuate while awaiting assaying and weighing. However, political and financial interests prevailed, and all that the government would permit was quarterly coinages and the creation of new coinage towns at Calstock, Hayle and St Austell. But even these 'reforms' were not enough and five years later the system collapsed and was never revived.

Little now remains of the halls in which these mysterious rites were practised for more than 600 years. Coining at Bodmin probably took place in the Great Hall of the medieval priory that stood until 1837 when it was demolished to make way for the present Assize Court. The coinage hall at Lostwithiel was likely to have been in the same building as the Stannary Court, part of which still exists at the corner of Quay Street and Fore Street. That at Liskeard was in Well Lane near the Town Hall and prison, but it has long since disappeared. At Truro it perhaps stood at the east end of Boscawen Street, though another view is that it was incorporated into the Town Hall that was completed in 1846. In Helston there is fairly conclusive evidence that the medieval Chapel of Our Lady in the centre of Lady Street was used for coining after its secularisation at the Reformation, though today the only physical record is the street that still bears the name of Coinage-hall. In Penzance a new coinage hall was built by the corporation after 1663 below the Market House and a new one near the quay in 1816, but again only the name Coinage-hall Street survives. At St Austell, which was a stannary town 1833–8, the assayer probably used the old Market House that was pulled down in 1844, while at Calstock and Hayle, since they also were coinage towns for only five years, he perhaps used any convenient building on his rounds.

Behind the mystique of coining lay that of smelting. Smelting would have been unnecessary had all tin come from streaming because that produced the purest tin of all for, when found, all the sulphides and arsenides had already been weathered out to produce what was called 'grain tin'. When heated it granulated and, in this form, was invaluable for making coloured glazes and in glassmaking. And, of course, where a stream cut its way to the sea, prospectors were always at hand to start their streaming, two of the most important areas for this type of recovery being in the Carnon Valley and in the Portreath Valley where in 1886 the Redruth Tin-Streaming Works managed no less than seventeen sites. Tin-streaming is still carried on, requiring much patience but little capital.

Smelting, however, was a different matter. The first smelters, in use before the fourteenth century, were known as blowing-houses and consisted of rough granite and turf structures with thatched roofs. Charcoal was heated in furnaces by means of bellows that were worked by hand or by a waterwheel, the molten tin being simply run off into granite moulds. While it is not unusual to come across tin-moulds, it is almost impossible now to trace in Cornwall the sites of these early blowing-houses, except where a name has survived such as Blowing-house Lane in St Austell (many sites, however, have been found on Dartmoor). But it is known from documentary sources that there were two at each of Calstock, Linkinghorne, St Neots, St Blazey, St Austell, St Stephen-in-Brannel, St Allen, Gwennap, Redruth, Illogan, Mawgan-in-Meneage, Breage, Ludgvan, Gulval, Bissoe, St Agnes, Penryn; Wendron and Kenwyn each had three, and others were at Charlestown, Gweek, Trannack, Ponsanooth, Cardinham, Sithney, Stithians, St Cleer, Porthtowan, Godolphin and Madron. In those days there was little to distinguish miner and smelter but, as mining deepened and became more costly and the reverberatory furnace came into production towards the end of the seventeenth century, the industry divided into two distinct arms. The 'black tinners' were those who produced black tin, that is tin concentrate after separation from the tin-stone following stamping and washing, and so-called from its black or dark-brown colour. They then sold it to the smelters who reduced it to white tin, the smelters consequently being called the 'white tinners'. It is not necessary here to detail how, as the industry became more complex, the smelters, through their mystiques of assaying and measuring and their knowledge of the metal market, became the bankers and merchants of the miners and adventurers, discounting the tin-bills at a profit to themselves and generally amassing more than moderate fortunes, so few were the risks they had to run compared with the unpredictability of shaft-mining.

Behind the physical remains of the smelting houses, therefore, lies the other side of the picture of tin mining that cannot be ignored. Fundamentally nothing now remains of the processes involved, but their small size is sufficient to demonstrate that the smelting of tin was never as complicated or as technically difficult or as costly as the smelting of copper. When the Geologists' Association visited Penzance in June 1871, they visited the smelter there and the manager, Mr A. K. Barnett, showed them the smelting process. The black tin mixed with culm was thrown into the furnace and kept stirred with a rabble. After six hours it was tapped and out ran the white metal and its slag. This was crude metallic tin. The crude metal was refined on the hearth of the furnace by liquidising it, after which the molten tin was tapped into a huge cast-iron kettle with a fire underneath it. Into this kettle, a large billet of green apple-wood was placed—a process called 'poling'. The whole of the hot metal boiled and splashed in all directions. This had the effect of bringing the dross to the surface when it was skimmed off and the pure refined metal was pressed into moulds to form tin ingots.

The smelting houses were sited, from about 1800 onwards, mainly in two areas, Truro and Penzance, though there were others. One at Portreath between 1813 and 1825 was started by Collan Harvey of St Day, brother-in-law of John Williams of Scorrier and partner of Williams, Foster & Co, copper smelters at Swansea, and there were three at St Austell. The Charlestown smelting house was established in 1834 by John Taylor to smelt ores from St Agnes and the mines of the Tamar Valley, and was later acquired by the Bolithos of Penzance; north-west of the harbour and close to Mount Charles, it closed down in 1884. In St Austell itself there were the New or Higher Blowing House at Trenance, owned by the Bolithos and Robert and William Mitchell, and the Old Blowing House, first owned by Fox's, Rashleigh & Co, and then acquired by Daubuz, William Harvey, Davey & Williams. William Harvey disposed of it in 1839, when the buildings became part of the St Austell Foundry, all of them still intact and in the ownership of Harvey & Co. The Lower Blowing House was in Pond-dhu Road.

In and around Truro there were at least eight smelting houses. Coosebea did not survive long and was finished by 1810, its buildings being converted into a woollen mill and then a paper mill until they were sold in 1847. Perran, whose site was at Tarrandean at the head of Mellingey Creek, was working in 1810 and then finished its life as an arsenic works. The Garras Wharf smelting house began activities about 1820 under the direction of George Grenfell and Henry Boase of Penzance, while the one at Trethellan was acquired by William

Harvey in 1838. Today there are three sites left where the physical remains are worth a visit and an examination. The Truro smelting house, begun in 1816, was east of the present St Austell Street and close by the navigable head of the River Allen where it entered Truro River; its layout on the ground can still be traced. Carvedras, acquired in 1818 by the most famous of the smelters, Theophilus Daubuz, and used by his family for almost eighty years, was situated almost underneath the old timber viaduct at the eastern end of the railway station at Truro, where it can still be seen with its general appearance not greatly changed, though the stacks have long since been thrown. Since it closed down in 1898 it has served as a creamery and is now a warehouse. At Calenick, a mile south of Truro at the head of a creek branching westwards from the Fal, were ten powerful furnaces owned by Thomas Daniell, but of these nothing now remains and the site is now marked by the charming clock-tower and the elegant home of the smelter adjoining, built c 1770.

In the Penzance neighbourhood there have existed six smelting houses. The most westerly, to serve the mines around St Just, was Trereife, more recently known as Stable Hobba, on the right-hand side of the road that leads up the coombe from Newlyn. Owned by John Batten of Penzance, it closed in 1896 and was subsequently used by a manufacturer of pharmaceutical products and is now a fish fertiliser factory. In Penzance itself at Chyandour was perhaps the most renowned of them all, built on the site of an old blowing-house and begun by the Tremenheeres of Castle Horneck, but associated throughout the nineteenth century with the Bolithos, a family of successful tanners, merchants, shipowners and importers from Falmouth. The smelting house has entirely disappeared and was on the site of a yard that is now used by a local firm of coal importers, but its lines are not difficult to reconstruct: the exterior wall, fronting the street and rounded to facilitate the passage of the waggons; the blacksmith's shop adjoining; the lines of original workers' cottages on both sides of the narrow road that leads to the village of Gulval; Ponsandane, the imposing home of the Bolithos, behind which were the stables, now flats, surmounted by a small clock-tower; and the granite horse-trough in the square, now the last reminder of the thousands of horses that were used in this heavy industry.

Eastwards from Penzance there was once a smelting house at Ludgvan, but there are no traces of this now. It was worked in the eighteenth century with Treloweth, a much bigger affair that was acquired by L. C. Daubuz in 1791 and which resisted closure until 1883. Its site was adjacent to the present Lamb & Flag at St Erth on the A30 and was, up to 1840, one of the most important tin smelters in Cornwall. It closed in 1883 and five years later was being used as a butter factory and creamery, promoted by the Bolithos. The site of the present Unigate creamery at St Erth station was a china-clay dry in the 1920s, and it became a creamery in 1935. The dairy company used some of the old smelter buildings by the Lamb & Flag for their transport depot. The 'hot-mark', ie trade-mark, of the smelter was the Lamb and Flag, now perpetuated in the name of the inn.

Hayle was a centre for smelting too. The smelter at Angarrack was established as early as 1704, in 1804 it was under the ownership of Richard Cunnack, William Carne, the Bolithos and James Pascoe, and disappeared after its closure in 1881. Trelissick, founded about 1820 by George Grenfell of Penzance and then leased by Charles Pascoe Grenfell, was situated beside Penpol stream near the present Post Office in Foundry Square and has also disappeared. However, some remains are left of the leading smelting house in Cornwall, Mellanear, established by William Harvey & Company in 1838 after he had parted from Daubuz. It was sited on Ropewalk Moor and can be found at the end of a short lane, lined by unpretentious late Georgian houses, one of which was occupied by William Harvey. Of the smelting house itself only one of the original buildings remains, a part of a wall, the granite support of the main gateway, and the old laboratory and office which are now dwelling-houses. It was last occupied by a manufacturer of surf-boards. The history behind this site, however, is not that of closure in the late nineteenth century corresponding with the closure of the mines. When Harvey & Company saw the writing on the wall and noticed that increasing shipments of tin from Bolivia were being discharged, not at Hayle, but at Liverpool, it was realised that the time had come to move from Hayle to Liverpool. So a site was found at Bootle, and there their smelting house flourishes today, their emblem still the Lamb and Flag, leaving Cornwall with not a single house to call its own. Ironically now, the two remaining tin mines, South Crofty and Geevor, have to send their black tin for refining to Bootle. Thus the smelting houses, like the mines, have come and gone, leaving on the ground an almost indelible pattern of the industry that for a very long time made Cornwall a power-house of the Industrial Revolution and then dispersed its workers throughout the mining areas of the world.

CHAPTER FIVE

Hayle—A New Industrial Town of the West

(*contributed by Edward Wigley*)

HAYLE is a brisk modern little town, situated by the estuary of the River Hayle and guarded from the sea by large sand dunes or 'towans'. It offers little in the way of 'picture card' beauty and to the visitor, hurrying along the A30 on his way to Land's End and St Ives, it probably passes unnoticed. To the discerning eye, however, it presents many fascinating features of an active industrial past.

Hayle came into existence in the latter half of the eighteenth century, when its name first began to appear on maps. The town is a product of the Industrial Revolution, and the combination of a maritime position, plus the surrounding mines, gave it life. The name Hayle (Heyl) is Cornish for estuary and, although the age of the town is not great, the history of the estuary goes back to the dim past, since it once formed part of an ancient trade route.

The River Hayle enters the estuary at the western end of the larger of two tidal lakes. Its channel skirts the shore and marks the boundary of Lelant parish. The smaller of the lakes lies to the east and forms what is now called the Copperhouse Pool. The Angarrack River flows into this and the lakes are joined by a narrow channel which leads to the sea. Midway between the lakes, a further stream, known as the Penpol River, flows in. At low water, acres of sand are uncovered, traversed by meandering channels which show clearly the changing drift. With the tide high, the lakes are full and possess a strange beauty of their own.

Across the Copperhouse Pool lies Phillack with its beautifully positioned church and the houses nestling around it. Phillack is a very old village, built on the very edge of the shifting sands of the towans. Over the years it has watched benignly the growth of industrial Copperhouse. It has seen it all—the copper furnaces, the foundry, the mills and the railway—and it has seen them all fade away leaving Copperhouse as it is today, with houses and building estates growing ever faster. The coast north of the estuary is very beautiful and visitors have long discovered the charm of the sand hills and the famous 'three miles of golden sands'. The towans extend past Gwithian and as far as the Red River, where they give place to low cliffs, rising to Godrevy Point.

Westward of Hayle, and on the opposite side of the river, lie Lelant and Carbis Bay with St Ives sparkling jewel-like in the distance. On a still evening the dark tower of Lelant church with its backdrop of green hills makes an unforgettable picture. To see Hayle in perspective, one should climb Trencrom, a wild and striking hill near Lelant from which the view over Hayle and Copperhouse to the east is particularly fine. The quays and old buildings show up clearly and, with a little imagination, one can see the old trading ships, with sails spread, making the harbour.

On such an exposed coast, the value of this land-locked harbour is very obvious. In spite of the shifting sand-bar and the difficult approach, it must have proved a boon and blessing many times in the past. In the old days, the quays were on the western bank of the river and Lelant was really the port. Remnants of the quays can be seen today and it is fairly certain that shipping came there as far back as the fourteenth century. The history of Hayle, however, starts on the eastern side where in about 1740 a company was formed by 'local men of substance' to trade and deal in mine merchandise. Coal and timber were much needed by the mines as well as ropes, limestone, bricks and many other commodities.

Hayle was ideal for a port—it was near the tin and copper mines and was a reasonable jumping-off place for the sea voyage to South Wales and Bristol. Only the sand gave trouble. Both wind and water

Hayle

Page 89 (above) *Interior of Tregargus china-stone mills showing grinding pans;* (below) *SS* Glenmary (*1921–58*) *loading blue elvan from the old stone pier at Porthoustock in August 1937*

The great granite viaduct over the Luxulyan Valley, built 1839–42 by J. T. Treffry and the first in Cornwall. It carried water to power turbines as well as a railway track, and is known as the Treffry Aqueduct; 660ft long

borne, it has always been the bane of the estuary, silting the sea channel and blocking the harbour with a shifting sand-bar. The company quays were situated on either side of the narrow channel joining the two tidal lakes. This was kept partially clear of sand by the two streams that flowed into it at low tide, but ships could only reach the quays at the spring tides and even then it was not always possible. However, in spite of difficulties, the company prospered. Other traders came and the foundation of Hayle as a port was laid, setting the stage for the next scene.

THE CORNISH COPPER COMPANY

Sporadic attempts had been made to smelt copper in Cornwall since the beginning of the seventeenth century. No great success was obtained but in 1754–5 Sampson Swaine, a metallurgist with experience of copper smelting, set up smelting furnaces at Carn Entral, near Camborne. His partners included such men as John Vivian, Christopher Hawkins, Sir John St Aubyn and others. The venture was successful but, although the furnaces were in a good position as regards the mines, the cost of bringing coal by packhorse from the quays at Hayle made the smelting costs too high. In 1757, therefore, the smelter was removed to a part of Trevassack Estate, bordering on the eastern arm of the Hayle estuary and carried on its trade under the name of the Cornish Copper Company. Houses were built for the workers and the area became known from that time as Copperhouse. A very useful by-product of the smelter was the copper slag or 'scoria'. This, when run off from the molten copper, was cast into moulds, making blocks 18in × 12in × 8in. If the employees of the copper company were prepared to build their own houses on land provided, the blocks were given to them. This offer must have helped in great measure to solve the housing problem.

The new arrangement worked well at first and the copper company built quays along the side of the Angarrack River. However, the feeling among mine adventurers that Cornish copper should be

F

smelted in Cornwall was basically wrong. Three to four times its weight in coal was needed to smelt a given weight of copper ore and this meant a great increase in the weight of coal to be shipped from Wales, although Leifchild in his *Cornwall and its Mines and Miners* gives 18–20 tons of fuel to get 1 ton of copper. It was true that tin had been successfully smelted in Cornwall for many years. The smelting of copper, however, was much more difficult. Five to six times more heat was needed in the first place and the whole process took longer and was more complicated. To give some idea, here is a contemporary account, taken from volume two of *A History of Cornwall* by Samuel Drew, of the process in use at the time among the twenty-five furnaces at Copperhouse, all of them reverberatory.

> First, the ore was calcined to remove the arsenic, four tons at a time for twelve hours. Four cwts of this went into a smelting furnace and after four hours, the slag was drawn off. A second charge was now introduced and the process continued until the total furnace charge was ten cwts. After a further four hours of heating, making twelve in all, the furnace was tapped, the slag drawn off and the melted charge proper run into water to break it up. This regulus is again calcined, two and a half tons at a time for 24 hours. In turn, this was further smelted in quantities of twelve cwts for six hours. The slag was drawn off and the furnace tapped into water. Again the regulus was calcined and re-smelted in twelve cwts lots for six hours. After the slag had been drawn off, the molten copper was cast in sand moulds to form pigs. These pigs, of coarse copper, were further re-smelted three more times, two tons at a time for six hours. Each time the copper became molten, charcoal was thrown on the surface to purify it. Following the last smelting, the copper was ladled into moulds and allowed to harden. More copper is ladled on to that and so on, making cakes of copper, easily separable when cold, and weighing roughly forty-eight pounds. The many calcinations removed the sulphur and arsenic and oxidized the iron and other substances present.

The kinds of copper leaving the works were tough cake, brass-cake, japan-copper (small bars having the colour of scarlet japan), shot-copper for making brass, bell-metal (copper and tin) and pot-metal (copper and lead). The whole process was extremely unhealthy for the men who worked at it. Little precaution was taken and the combination of heat and arsenic fumes must have had an appalling effect. Cakes and ingots of copper were sent to the battery and rolling mills at Treloweth, 2 miles away in St Erth. The mill had three pairs of sheet rolls, one of bolt rolls. There were also two large trip hammers, one of 7cwt which could strike 100 blows a minute. Another machine was used for making wire. All the machinery was worked by water and the output of the mill was said to have been 700 tons a year. In fact, it was usually about 400.

The copper company would have failed as smelters at a much earlier date had it not been for the force of character of one man. He was John Edwards of Ludgvan, who became a managing partner in 1765. It was said of him that he could 'obtain ascendancy over most persons on all occasions' and this was probably true. At any rate, under his forceful guidance, the copper company kept going in spite of many setbacks. In the early 1780s Merchant Curnow, one of the original partners of the 1740 trading company, and now owner, died. The copper company negotiated and took over the two quays and all his other interests and thus at one stroke obtained a second trade as general and mine merchants.

In order that ships might more easily come up to the Copperhouse quays the company deepened and widened the Angarrack River channel in 1769, making a canal, half a mile long from Copperhouse to Hayle. To keep the canal free of sand they built small floodgates at the Ventonleague end and, by letting the impounded water rush out through sluices, were able to wash away at least part of the sand in the canal. Up to 1788 Hayle harbour was rarely accessible to vessels of more than 70 tons. In 1788, the company built a weir across the entrance of the Copperhouse Pool and erected floodgates on its southern side. By the aid of these, the incoming tide could be trapped in the pool and released at low water. The force of water washed away the sand and this time helped to keep the harbour and the sea channel free. In 1790 the company made Custom House Road and it is said they made the first swing bridge over the canal mouth. In 1808, two more floodgates were put in on the north side of the weir and this doubled the force of water and greatly assisted in the removal of sand. Vessels of 120 tons could now come up to the copper works, those of 250 tons could get as far as the coal quays. In 1811, Black Road was built across the Pool to the foot of Phillack Churchtown hill. It was so called from the slag that was used to make it. Later, it was continued to the northern quays; by using this the copper company was able to avoid the tolls of the public roads.

This, then, was the state of affairs at the copper company in the early 1800s, its activities driven along by Edwards' personality and force of will. The smelting side of the business was now beginning to fail and the owners were exploiting their second string as mine merchants with all dispatch. It is certain they would not have tolerated competition from anyone without a struggle and it is at this point that the third phase of the story of Hayle begins.

HARVEY'S FOUNDRY AND RIVALRY

To get the picture we must go back again to the latter years of the eighteenth century, at which time Cornwall had no real engineering or foundry facilities of its own. The great pumping engines for the mines were made in the iron foundries of the Midlands and brought down by sea. But John Harvey, a Cornish blacksmith with a forge at Carnhell Green, a village about 3 miles from Hayle, saw clearly the advantages that would be gained by a local foundry. Hayle—being on the sea and close to the mines—was, as we have seen, an ideal site. So it was that in 1779 John Harvey moved to Hayle and built a small ironworks at Carnsew, on the southern side of the estuary and between the Hayle and Penpol Rivers. In the building of the works, it must be remembered that Harvey was a smith in the broadest sense of the word. He would have turned his hand to anything, from masonry to carpentry, as well as all the skills needed in the forge. Without this versatility, the expense of setting up the works would have been far beyond his means.

An old story tells us that the start was made possible by a local squire, Sir John St Aubyn. It seems that Sir John, who was out hunting one Sunday morning before going to church, had lost a silver buckle off his shoe. Passing the forge at the time, he told John Harvey about the loss and the smith, without further ado, beat him out a new buckle from a silver spoon. Sir John was so impressed with Harvey's skill that he assisted with the start of the venture at Hayle. This is only legend but it could have a certain amount of truth in it.

One of the great needs of the Cornish mines at that time was iron pump-pipes. D. Rhys Phillips in his *History of the Vale of Neath* states that Harvey was sending scrap metal from Hayle to Neath in exchange for cast-iron pump parts in 1776. Many mines were still using wooden pipes made from hollowed-out trees and these gave constant trouble. One can be seen in the Folk Museum at Hayle Secondary School. In Shropshire the Coalbrookdale Company had been making cast-iron pipes for many years, but their cost, plus the cost of transport, limited their use in Cornwall. It was Harvey's ambition to cast these parts at Hayle; mastering the difficult art of ironfounding he succeeded in doing this and began to turn out pipes and engine parts. At first the Cornish Copper Company viewed with favour the start of the foundry, looking upon it as a potential customer for coal and iron.

Over the next ten years the foundry grew and prospered. John Harvey lost his three elder sons, leaving only Henry who was fifteen. Three of the girls married, Joanna to William West, a clever mining engineer; Anne to John Harvey, a cabinet-maker from Helston and no relation; and Jane to Richard Trevithick. William West and Richard Trevithick were close friends and companions. In Cornwall, steam-engines were rapidly increasing in number and the Boulton & Watt engine, with its separate condenser, soon ousted the old Newcomen. The engines were usually made in parts at different foundries and afterwards fitted on the mine itself. The prospect for engineering in Cornwall was now very bright.

The Hayle Foundry grew busier, but there were ever increasing difficulties in obtaining iron and coal. The Cornish Copper Company had by now eliminated all other competition and had a virtual mono-

poly of the mine trade. To break this, John Harvey bought a sloop of
his own, the *Providence*. With this, he traded direct for his coal and
iron. This move soon aroused the suspicions of the redoubtable John
Edwards of the copper company, who saw that the next step would
be the entry of Harvey into the mine-merchant trade as a direct
competitor. Edwards moved instantly and by clever dealing obtained
all that part of Carnsew north of the foundry. He also laid claim to
the foreshore rights of Carnsew. This meant that the only way Harvey
could get his ship to the foundry was up the Penpol River—and then
only at the highest tide. The battle was now on—a battle which was
to last for thirty years and which laid the foundation of the feud
between Copperhouse and Foundry—a feud, which to a mild extent
has lasted to the present day.

In spite of all this Harvey did enter the field as a mine-merchant
and he chartered other ships to meet the increased trade. When the
tides were low they discharged their cargoes on the sand-banks and
cart and packhorse served to deliver to the foundry. The firm prospered and Henry Harvey was now getting old enough to look after
the administrative side. He was proving himself an able business man.
Goods that the foundry dealt in at that time included bricks, slates,
pantiles, tools, nails, oil, soap, cooking pots, fire grates, coal, iron and
timber. Harvey pressed on. He had a new brig built at Bideford,
called the *Henry*, and trade further increased. A lighter was built with
low draught so that it could come up the Penpol River at lower tides.
The copper company actively opposed this and threw some of the
timber from her into the sea. They also blocked up the leat which
carried off the overflow from the waterwheel working the boring
mill—putting it out of action.

In 1803 John Harvey died at the age of seventy-three and his son
Henry took over from him. Four years later John Edwards died and
his successor was Joseph Carne, a man of similar temperament. The
feud continued unabated, with the copper company doing all it could
to hinder the progress of the foundry. Law suits, injunctions and
price-cutting were the order of the day. However, Henry Harvey was

an astute business man and a worthy opponent for Joseph Carne. Under his guidance the firm continued to grow in spite of setbacks. The Watt patents had expired in 1800 and the development of the Cornish engine could now progress unhindered. Richard Trevithick carried out many of his experiments with high-pressure steam at Harvey's foundry, and the parts of his famous road carriage, that climbed Camborne hill under steam in 1801, were made there.

In the 1820s, the copper company turned to pastures new. Copper-smelting had finished, so they started a foundry of their own, incorporating some of the old buildings. To obtain skilled labour for the venture they offered more money to Harvey's employees and succeeded in enticing many of them. The foundry was a success and made many famous engines, trading under the name of Sandys, Carne & Vivian and employing some 300 men. Today very little remains of the copperworks or the foundry. The sluice gates and the canal are still there and the slag blocks make a permanent memorial. Preserved at Kew by the Metropolitan Water Board is a magnificent 90in pumping-engine, designed by Thomas Wicksteed (1806–71), engineer of the East London Water Works, and made by this foundry in 1846. It worked for 97 years.

Henry Harvey had by this time built himself quite a large fleet of trading ships and in 1831 he and others started the steam-packet service between Hayle and Bristol with the steamship *Herald*. This was a great success and other ships followed, including rival steamers. Fares to Bristol were 21s (£1.05) single for cabin passengers and 9s (45p) for deck. The passage took about twenty hours. The packet service became a feature of Hayle and provided a fast link. It is interesting to note that a Mr Sharrock Semmens Dupen, purser to the boats, was the first person (in 1837) to take Cornish garden produce and dispose of it in the big towns. In 1858, 30,000 dozen broccoli were sent off in one week by steam-packet from Hayle. The remains of the packet quays can still be seen and it is only recently that the Steam Packet Hotel was demolished.

In spite of strong opposition Harvey had now built the long Penpol

quay and deepened the Penpol channel. Ships could now come up to
the foundry with little trouble. A tidal catchment pool had been built
on the Carnsew side and tide-gate and sluices permitted Harvey to
keep the sea channel clear without recourse to the rival company.

In 1833–4 the foundry built the famous Austen 80in pumping-
engine to designs which had, in fact, been formulated by Richard
Trevithick some twenty years before. It was built for the Fowey
Consols mine and it was undoubtably a fine example of a Cornish
engine. Such was its efficiency and fame that it attracted the attention
of Thomas Wicksteed and, as a result of this, many Harvey engines
were used to pump London's water. Other famous engines were made
for the Dutch government to drain the Haarlem Meer. One of these,
the Cruquius engine of 1849 with a 12ft diameter cylinder, is still
preserved at Vijfhuizen in Holland. A plate on the engine bears the
name 'Harvey & Co., Makers, Hayle Foundry'. At Kew are also to be
found two of Harvey's engines, a 70in of 1859 and the very large
100in of 1869.

Richard Trevithick died in April 1833 at Dartford. He had virtually
severed all connection with Hayle and three years later his widow,
Jane, gave up the White Hart Hotel there which she had managed for
some years, and retired. This original inn, built in 1824, is now the
Masonic Hall; the present White Hart Hotel alongside in Foundry
Square was built in 1836.

The Coming of the Railway

Originally all foundry transport to and from the multiplicity of
nearby mines was horsedrawn along tracks and roadways and both
foundries kept a large number of horses and mules for this purpose.
In 1834, however, an act of parliament was sought and granted to
make a railway from Hayle to Redruth with branches to Portreath and
Tresavean. A detailed description of the path of this mineral railway
was given on pages 30–31. Locomotives were employed from the
start, east of the Angarrack incline, but by 1842 they were used

throughout. In 1838 the Copperhouse Foundry built its first locomotive *Cornubia*.

The line, opened in December 1837, started as a narrow-gauge
railway, seven years later it was realigned to carry passengers as well
as goods from Hayle to Redruth. The railway company was said to
possess 5 locos, 119 trucks and 6 passenger carriages. This opening
on 22 May 1843 was a great occasion as all travel was free. Trucks and
carriages were used—the latter being reserved for 'those who were
fortunate or considered sufficiently respectable to get places'. The
same source also says 'the trucks were clustered like bees and the
closed carriages resembled the hold of a slave ship. All, however,
seemed pleased, so great is the charm of gratuitous amusement.' In
1849 no less than 57,018 passengers availed themselves of the new
service.

The company was one of the first to run 'excursions' and these
went from Redruth and Camborne to the beaches at Hayle. They
were very popular for Sunday school treats and a delightful verse of
a poem 'Life of the Rev Thomas Colins' by the Rev Samuel Coley
(1868) tells why:

> We shall see the rolling ocean,
> We shall breathe the fresh sea air,
> See, the country comes to greet us,
> And the swallows can't outfly,
> Houses, trees and hedges greet us,
> Running by, and running by.
> Happy Camborne!
> Where the railway is so nigh.

In Hayle the line started from Foundry Square, went along Penpol
Terrace and over the water at the Copperhouse sluice by a drawbridge. It then progressed along the northern side of the pool over
what is now the King George V Memorial Walk graced by several
houses of Regency design, crossed the present A30 truck road on the
level by the Penmare Hotel and so continued to Angarrack, climbing
the hill by means of a steam-drawn incline. As the Hayle Railway the
line had a short life. It was taken over by the West Cornwall Railway

in 1846. They re-routed it, cutting out the Angarrack and other inclines and building viaducts instead. It can be said, however, that the railway played its part in the achievement of an unbroken line from London to Penzance.

The original station at Hayle—it became an Institute after 1860— was preserved up to the end of World War II. The booking-hall, not demolished until 1950, lay almost underneath the present viaduct. The track of the original line is still visible and the Angarrack Incline scars the side of the valley. The line along Penpol Terrace has only recently been taken up and British Rail worked horsedrawn trucks over it for many years after the last war. The old drawbridge was replaced by a swing bridge which took both road and rail over the water. This bridge, opened in May 1877, is quite intact with all its lifting and turning mechanism and it carries a British Rail spur down to the quays. Four hundred and fifty pumps are required to raise the pressure in the piston to 240lb per sq in, which then raises the bridge so that it can be swung by chains.

THE END OF THE RIVALRY

Before his death in 1850, Henry Harvey handed over everything to his nephews and nieces, vesting the control in the hands of three trustees. In 1867 the foundry at Copperhouse closed down from lack of work and the business, quays and foundry passed into the Harveys' hands at an auction sale in February 1875. The horses were sold at Copperhouse Fair in September 1867 and shortly afterwards the foundry itself went for scrap.

The mines were failing and Harveys, too, were feeling the pinch. They enlarged their shipbuilding side and were able to build ships up to 4,000 tons. Even this did not save them and in November 1903 the foundry business went the way of their old rivals at Copperhouse and was sold up. As merchants they carried on and exist in strength today. The closure of the foundry was a great blow to the district.

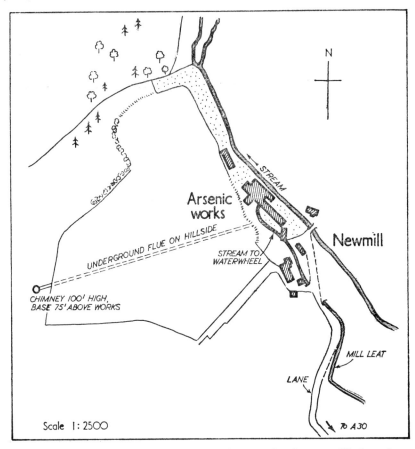

English Arsenic Company's works at Roseworthy, between Hayle and Camborne. See Gazetteer, p 250

In the past, Hayle has had many industries. Mines surrounded it, from the famous Wheal Alfred on the high ground behind to Wheal Lucy on the towans. There were tin smelters, arsenic works, a glass factory, Nobel's dynamite works, Ellis's brewery, flour mills and a biscuit factory. One engineering firm, J. & F. Pool Ltd, founded in 1848, and which made perforated metal and wire sieves for the mines, has survived the years and continues in greater strength. The others have all gone.

It was in such places as Hayle that the true spirit of Cornwall lay. The twilight came on its industry but it was a twilight after a long sunny day—a day that will be long remembered in history and legend.

CHAPTER SIX

China Clay—A Dynamic Industry

THE face of about 45 square miles of mid-Cornwall, spread out like a huge open fan with St Austell at its centre, has been transformed over the past 200 years into a 'lunar' landscape, characterised by great deep pits and quarries, and huge grey pyramids of waste material. Just as the excavations go down to 300ft, so do the mountains of waste raise their heads an equal distance. This part of Cornwall, stretching from Fraddon and Meledor in the west 9 miles eastwards to St Blazey, and from near Roche in the north for 5 miles southwards to High Street, St Stephen, has a peculiar fascination for those who have any sort of interest in mining or geology. Its many water-filled pits, ancient waste tips slowly being clothed by natural growth, villages large and small and its hamlets all display the unmistakable character of mining settlements, but above all, its incredibly active workings of this latter half of the twentieth century testify to a long period of industrial activity.

In the 1740s, a traveller returned from Virginia, one of Britain's North American colonies, bringing with him a sample of 'china clay'. This he showed to a Quaker chemist of Kingsbridge in South Devon, William Cookworthy (1705–80), who started his historic quest for this mineral in Cornwall somewhere about 1745. The exact year is not known, but writing about 1767, he records that it was at Tregonning Hill near Germoe about twenty years previously that he found the stone containing the special and peculiar properties of 'kaolin'. The traditional place is Wheal Grey, lying on the north side of the present A394 road (Penzance–Helston) about a mile west of Ashton, which became an active clay works in later years, even up to the 1920s.

Of special interest is the fact that Francis Egerton, 3rd Duke of

Bridgewater and 'father of inland navigation', advised Wedgwood not to apply to Parliament for a licence to import china clay from Cherokee Indian territory in America, of which he had received a sample in 1766, but to commission an agent to go there and negotiate with the Indians. In July 1767, Thomas Griffiths sailed for Charleston in South Carolina arriving in September. On 14 January 1768 he loaded a waggon train with 5 tons of clay at Ayoree in Cherokee territory (in the western tip of North Carolina) and brought it safely back to England by April. The total cost worked out at £130 per ton and was impractical bearing in mind the development of the Cornish clay, and so no more was shipped across the Atlantic. Griffiths later became Wedgwood's agent at St Stephen in Cornwall.

Cookworthy later on found a better stone for china manufacture at the Carloggas Quarry near St Stephen-in-Brannel. He used two words for it, 'petuntse' which is Chinese for feldspar, and 'caulin' or 'kaolin'. The former was ground in mills to a fine powder which was then mixed with the latter. He took out his first patent in 1768, establishing a china factory in Plymouth that year but moving to Bristol in 1769. It should also be mentioned in this context that it was in this period of Georgian history, an era that produced so much of our landscape and elegant buildings, that the famous potteries, Chelsea, Derby and Worcester were established using first ball-clays from Dorset and Devon. The great pioneer of English china and porcelain, Josiah Wedgwood, also came to Cornwall in search of china clay in the 1770s and Susan Martyn of Falmouth, in a Gorsedd prize essay, has recorded that the Staffordshire potteries were using clay from works at Breage and St Austell as early as 1759. There can still be seen the remains of a clay pit known as Minton where another famous Staffordshire pottery, established in 1793, once obtained its raw material, probably soon after 1800 as Thomas Minton was in Cornwall in 1798 or 1799. It lies adjacent to the Trelavour clay sett.

Side by side with the development of tin and copper mining in the second half of the eighteenth century in Cornwall, was the production of china-stone by normal methods of quarrying, and of the china clay or kaolin by open-cast mining. In the latter, after removal of the over-burden, water was led to the top of the working face or stope by a timber launder. As it drained down the face of soft decomposed rock, workers using chisel-pointed picks known as dubbers and two-pronged hoes, cut out strakes or gullies. As these deepened through the action of the water, the mass of rock fell in, dropped to the foot of the stope, and more water coming in from above began to break up the lumps. The coarse mass, containing quartz, feldspar and tourma-line, was then run into separating pits, the three waste minerals just mentioned dropped to the bottom, and the clay slurry flowed out into a series of narrow channels or drags. At intervals along the channel was a small weir or riffle, and as the slurry passed through, there was a further deposition of solids, mainly mica. A characteristic of the clay district landscape are these large 'micas', and associated settlement tanks and other receptacles for further purifying the clay.

CLAY PORTS AND MINERAL LINES

Towards the end of the eighteenth century, Cornishmen, much to the forefront in mineral exploitation, were on the mark to realise the value of this new mineral. Clay had been shipped from the beach at West Polmear near St Austell to the pottery at Bristol, and it was Charles Rashleigh of Menabilly who conceived the idea of building a new harbour here in 1790. Over the next decade, this came to fruition, and indeed a new township was built, to be called Charles-town and which had a population of about 1,000 at the turn of the century. Valuable cargoes of china clay and copper ore, the products of local clay works and the Charlestown Mines, were sent to smelters and potteries from 1819. Clay is still shipped from this harbour, designed by John Smeaton FRS at the end of his life, for he died in 1792.

The development of the industry continued and, by 1807, St Stephen had seven active clay works and the nearby Trethosa Works was producing 300 tons of clay per year. In 1813, a Dr Fitton was writing of works both at St Stephen and St Dennis: four years later, the celebrated Dr John Paris, much associated with Penzance and President of the Royal Cornwall Polytechnic, recorded that the West of England Clay Company were paying Lord Grenville mineral dues to the value of £7,000 a year, a handsome sum in Regency times. John Lovering, a name that became famous in Cornish clay circles, came to the duchy at this period and was engaged in raising chinastone in 1815.

During this early period of mineral working for the pottery industry, it is of interest to record that for about seventy years after 1750, soapstone or steatite, which Andrew Ure MD, *Dictionary of Chemistry* (1823), called 'a species of Rhomboidal mica', and which was found in Cornish serpentine, was obtained by shaft mining at Gew Graze, Kynance, at Trethvos on Predannack Downs and other places in the vicinity of the Lizard. It was not only used in porcelain manufacture, but also in cosmetics and for fulling cloth.

The need for facilities for exporting clay by sea began to be seen at this time: Charlestown, the new port for St Austell, having been established for about twenty-five years. Sir Christopher Hawkins of Trewithen, perhaps not to be outdone by the Rashleighs, built his own new port at Pentewan, a few miles up the coast from Mevagissey, completing it in 1826. Its main purpose was to provide the means for ships to bring in coal and to load china clay and other mining produce. As a port it was never a success due to silting in the shipping channel, but it was the southern terminus of a new railway from St Austell completed in 1829, the third in Cornwall, and which did not cease to run until almost ninety years later. Incidentally, Mevagissey itself was a clay port in the early 1800s.

As we have seen (pp 38–9) the outstanding Cornish personality in the engineering field was Joseph Thomas Treffry of Fowey who was so much associated with great mining enterprises all around the Fowey and St Blazey districts. In the decade after 1829, he financed and built an entirely new port, Par, to provide an outlet for his copper, granite and china clay (pp 39–40). It came into use from 1833, the

Page 107   (above) *The sea-lock on the Bude Canal, giving access from the sea into the harbour basin;* (below) *photograph taken in 1906 of the construction of the concrete-block viaduct across the river Tamar at Calstock for the Plymouth Devonport & South-Western Junction Railway. The contractor was J. Chas Lang of Liskeard, and over 11,000 concrete blocks, made on the site, were used. It is 117ft high*

Page 108 (above) *Camelford railway station about 1950 as built by the North Cornwall Railway 1893–4;* (below) *Royal Albert Bridge and steam ferry, Saltash, October 1953. One of these ferry boats is now doing duty at King Harry Ferry over the Fal*

engineer was J. M. Rendel, and today it is one of the three china-clay ports of Cornwall.

During the canal age, Treffry had had a route surveyed in 1815 for a canal which he hoped to build from the profitable Fowey Consols Mines at Tywardreath, which he purchased in 1822, to the port of Padstow. Nothing came of this, but a short canal was built in the 1840s from Par to the foot of the Carmears Incline (p 133).

In 1839, Treffry commenced his mineral railway across Cornwall from St Blazey, constructing the first great granite viaduct that Cornwall had ever seen across the Luxulyan Valley between 1839 and 1842 (plate, p 90). This magnificent engineering work, that today stands as a monument to Cornish engineering skill, is 660ft long, and carried both a railway and an aqueduct underneath the rail track over the valley on ten arches of 40ft span and at a maximum height of almost 100ft above the valley floor. The aqueduct carried water that was led by a leat down the side of the valley for over a mile to Pont's Mill, near Tywardreath Highway, where it provided the power for the water turbines to crush china-stone. Treffry's railway from St Blazey and up the Carmears Incline ran across the viaduct to Luxulyan, Bugle and Indian Queens, where it was joined by his tramway from Hendra Downs, St Dennis, and then across country to the new harbour at Newquay. This, in itself, was a further example of Cornish engineering achievement, involving two tunnels.

Mr George Starke of St Dennis, who has long been interested in these early days of clay working, an industry in which he has spent all his working life, has discovered and contributed the following information:

A stonemason named Rodda of St Blazey, who was greatly addicted to the bottle and who was 'saved' by the Bible Christians, was employed by Treffry about 1838. In 1839, the new south pier at Newquay had been severely damaged in a gale and Rodda was sent to undertake repair work. The Luxulyan viaduct had been started in 1839, and two tunnel contracts were let the following year; that of a Mr Barry in March 1840 for the incline tunnel that connected the harbour quay with the top of the cliff at Newquay, and the second, the tunnel at Toldish at Indian Queens which was started

G

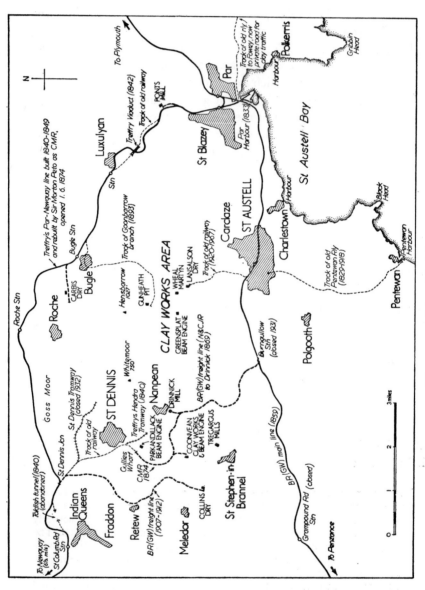

The extent of the china clay area

in August 1840. This was 11 ft high and 8 ft 6 ins in width. (It is still extant though disused as the later railway by-passed it to the north). In October 1840, Treffry agreed a price with a Mr Leach to lay the new line at 10d per lineal fathom. Rodda was one of the masons employed.

It seems certain therefore that the earlier of Treffry's mineral railways was this one from Hendra Downs to Newquay. Its southern terminus was at Gullies Wharf, 185/949572, Hendra Prazey, St Dennis, and one can still see the railway bridge here over the road, the original of 1840 and the later 1873–4 extension on the west side by the Cornwall Minerals Railway. Gullies Wharf is now all grass-grown, but the stone-faced loading platform is still there and the remains of a gate post made of old tram-rails. It was from this wharf that trains were drawn up an incline to the clay pit at Hendra Downs by a stationary engine, and there is a photograph of March 1933 in the late Mr Kendall Andrew's collection, showing the beam engine, built in William West's foundry at St Blazey and erected in the Hendra engine house in 1857, that operated the mineral trains to and from Gullies Wharf. The remains of the engine house, perched on the edge of a cliff face overlooking a deep water-filled pit is all that remains today of this early mining enterprise, although part of the railway embankment north of Gullies Wharf at Hendra Prazey is visible as well as a granite slab bridge that carried Treffry's line over a 'cattle-creep'.

Apart from these activities of Treffry's, an extensive mileage of such lines was built during the nineteenth century to serve the clay industry that has steadily increased its activities over two hundred years. The longest was the section from Burngullow on the Plymouth–Penzance main line (where there was a station until 1931) to St Dennis junction at the western end of Goss Moor. About 7 miles in length it was started by William West & Co (St Blazey foundry) in 1865 who built the first 3 miles at the southern end. Today it only exists as far as Gullies Wharf.

From St Dennis Junction in a due southerly direction is a length of 4 miles of railway that still serves the extreme western area of the clay district running through Retew as far as Collins' dries, Meledor. Another line, now taken up, ran from the Newquay branch line near Bugle station through Stenalees and finished at the Gunheath Pit. Another mineral line ran for 2 miles, leaving the main line half a mile west of St Austell station, and traversing the valley up to Ruddlemoor near Carthew. In the northern tip of the district, a branch siding ran from near Bugle Station into the dries and brick and tile works at Carbis; this is still operative, and two other short branches, again still extant, run from the Burngullow branch into Goonvean dries and another into the English Clay's works at Drinnick. Treffry's line from Pont's Mill to Luxulyan station has long been taken up. One further railway used for clay traffic is the Wenford mineral line, opened as far back as 1834 as part of the Bodmin & Wadebridge Railway. It runs up the valley of the River Camel through Helland Bridge to Wenford clay dries and just beyond to the terminus at Wenford Bridge. It is still operative and is now the most northerly point of the railway system in Cornwall.

Of the clay industry in the middle of the nineteenth century, Mrs R. M. Barton, to whom so much is owed for her masterly *History of the Cornish China Clay Industry*, has painted this vivid picture:

> A scene then probably unique in the world. In all directions lay busy clay pits, round and oval ones: square pans filled with liquid clay: overhead launders (long wooden troughs for carrying liquid) attached to pumps forming a skeleton roof: the constant passage of bonnetted and aproned women carrying clay blocks to reeders, drying sheds or drying grounds. Children, who earned 7d a day, collected moss to fill the joints between the granite blocks of the pans which allowed moisture to pass through. The creaking of pumps, of horse whims and the rushing of countless water engines.

In the middle of this century, the industry employed 7,000 men, women and children.

TECHNICAL ADVANCES
Washing and Drying

After the early methods of washing the decomposed granite down the face of the stope (p 114), the low-pressure water jet was developed, and then after further experiments in the 1870s, the high-pressure monitor-jet now working at pressures up to 300lb per sq in, operated by gravity in deep pits and by pumps in shallower ones. But the actual method used for the first part of the clay process remains the same. The liquid mass runs into sand drags to deposit the waste, and the slurry containing about 2 per cent clay is then pumped up to the surface, to be run, in a few remaining clay works, into micas and settling tanks. The end product is a 'lardy-clay' located in tanks next to the dry. As soon as it has reached a consistency where it can be shovelled into trucks, it is taken into the dry, a long single-storey building, again a characteristic of this district, and frequently 300–400ft long.

The dry contains a number of large furnaces at one end together with a stoke hold. The hot gases of combustion are drawn through a long duct covered with special tiles, $2\frac{1}{2}$–5in thick, and pass into a typically Cornish engine-house chimney stack at the other end. The clay is spread out on the tiled pan and, when dry, is then shovelled out into the linhay, a long extension of the building parallel with the drying floor but on the opposite side to the conditioning tanks. In a big dry, there was storage room for 1,000 tons, and it was to many of these dries that the railways came, bringing in coal and carrying away the clay. At Parkandillack, the Goonvean & Rostowrack China Clay Co Ltd, ever mindful of the historic heritage of Cornish industry, have preserved the remains of what is generally believed to be the first coal-kiln in Britain. It has a notice board inscribed: 'This dry, built circa 1848 by Charles Truscott is reputed to be the first artificially-heated china clay kiln in the United Kingdom. The pan area being 9 ft × 9 ft was able to dry approximately 8 tons per week.'

The invention of electric lighting in 1853 led John Lovering, in the late 1870s, to experiment in its use for clay washing by night at the Ninestones Pit, and St Austell in 1886 was the first Cornish town to have its own electricity supply. Bearing in mind the dynamism of Joseph Treffry the creator of Par in the 1830s, it is slightly curious

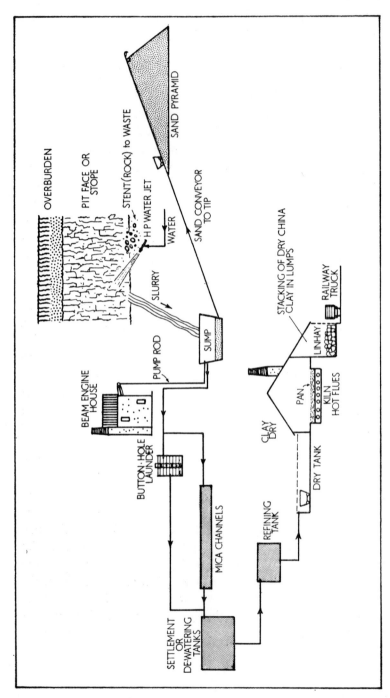

Flow diagram of china clay production as it was done until about twenty years ago and still is in a few pits

to read in Kelly's Directory of 1923 that the streets of Par were still then lit with oil lamps!

The transmission of materials in liquid form by underground pipe line has become a feature of our own part of the twentieth century, eg chalk-slurry pumped for 57 miles from the Kensworth Quarry in South Bedfordshire to the cement kilns at Rugby. Sixty years ago, John Lovering built a large dry at Charlestown Harbour and pumped clay slurry to it from tanks at Carclaze through a pipe 1½ miles long, but the principle had been propounded in the 1850s. Parkyn's dry at Burngullow Station was similarly connected by pipe to the pit 400yd away, but a much longer pipeline, over 3 miles in length, brought clay from the pit at Plenderleath near Towednack to the dry at St Erth station. This was in production in the 1920s, and although the clay works have gone, superseded by an important creamery, the pipe still supplies it with water. The Stannon clay works still pumps clay 6 miles to the dries at Wenford, indeed there are now miles of pumping mains from clay works to Par and Charlestown.

Water-power

Any study of the history of industry and technology during the eighteenth century reveals the skill of the millwright, afterwards to be called the mechanical engineer. Many such became extraordinarily skilful in using water-power and in developing hydraulic machinery. The waterwheel was used extensively throughout the whole of the Cornish clay-mining industry, both on the surface and underground, not only for winding, crushing and grinding, but also for pumping. Water was led down hundreds of yards of timber launders in order to provide power to turn wheels that in turn operated pumps to lift the liquid clay slurry from considerable depths to the surface. A description of the one remaining 'Cornish Lift' (liquid pump) in working order is on page 123.

The simplest pump of all was the 'flop-jack', a beam-engine where one end of the beam (or bob) was connected to the pumping rod, whilst the other carried a tank. A launder provided the tank with water and, on becoming full the tank dropped, pulling the bob up thus raising the pump rod. At the lowest level, the bottom of the tank impinged on a valve which released the water. The rod then descended bringing up the bucket (or tank) and the cycle began again. And, gradually, when Cornish engine pioneers came into their own, steam power was used, for here was a really practical use for their great machines that were able to lift, continuously night and day, great quantities of clay slurry from the sump of the deepest clay pits.

There is probably no better visual record of a large part of the Cornish clay industry fifty years ago, than that provided by a 70 page brochure of about 1922 by English China Clays Ltd, the company incorporated in April 1919, but whose origins go back to 1837. At that period of its history, the firm had storage capacity for 100,000 tons of dry clay, china-stone and ground china-stone, and over 200,000 tons of wet clay in tanks. Its complement of engines, water-, gas- and steam-powered, were capable of pumping over 1 million gallons per hour, from a total horse power of nearly 4,000, and in addition winding capacity exceeding 2½ million tons. Its dries totalled 2 miles in length with a drying capacity of half a million tons per year, and it owned houses for workers sufficient to shelter 1,600 people. Moreover its brick kilns were capable of producing 4½ million bricks a year, though most of them were from the Lee Moor works in Devon, where the company owned the world's largest clay pit.

At this period many large beam engines were pumping clay at such works as Dorothy, Whitemoor; Great Beam at Bugle; Virginia, Meledor; Dubbers Pit near Nanpean; Little Treviscoe and Trethosa, both at St Stephen; as well as the engines in work at Goonvean, Parkandillack, Carpalla, Blackpool and Greensplat clay works. Huge waterwheels, used for pumping, were at work all over the clay district, and English China Clays recorded that 'at one time, the industry was very dependent upon these wheels, and in many cases, they still [1922] serve useful purposes'. Examples of these magnificent water engines were to be found at the clay works at Melbur, North Carloggas, Virginia, Stannon near Wenford Bridge and Treviscoe. They used flat-rod transmission, the crank on the shaft of the wheel driving rods backwards and forwards over long distances in order to provide horizontal motion that was converted into vertical motion by bell cranks. Practically no examples remain today.

These records show that, half a century ago, water-power, steam engines and gas engines reigned supreme. Today, the diesel engine and electric power have superseded them. In March 1927, the first electric pumps were installed at the Dorothy clay pit, Whitemoor, pumping 60,000 gallons an hour from 300ft down.

Housing and Specialised Equipment

The history of this specialised clay-mining industry is part of the social history of Britain, and English Clays, since their pits and works were often far from towns, 'had to erect many cottages for the accommodation of their workers'. It owned 400 houses in the St Austell clay district half a century ago, and most of them stand today as a memorial of a great industry's development.

China-clay working required special tools and special clothing, and at Nanpean there was a boot manufactory. It was established because of the difficulty in obtaining the heavy handmade boots for use in washing and working in the tanks. At St Stephen, there was special patented equipment for sharpening drills, and a cooperage at Burngullow for manufacturing casks used at that time for exporting clay. The port of Charlestown used to import large amounts of barrel staves from the Baltic for this cooperage, but the replacement of casks by paper sacks or bags which started about fifty years ago gradually ended this old trade.

THE ARCHAEOLOGICAL REMAINS

Earlier chapters in this book have told of the decline of metal mining in Cornwall. The clay industry on the other hand has steadily increased its potential over the two centuries since it started, and whereas in the 1820s it produced 20,000 tons a year, a century and a half later the figure is a hundred times that amount. The reason is easy to find: clay has a great many uses, eg in the manufacture of rubber, plastics, paint, pharmaceuticals, inks and dyes, whilst the largest proportion goes into papermaking.

There are now comparatively few remains of the archaeology of the early clay industry—so much of its history is being swallowed up or bulldozed by the giant machines characteristic of our present-day engineering methods. The race for more and more clay is reckoned more important than conservation of the history of an industry that is now so important to Cornwall. In the early days, eight *months* was needed from the raising of the clay in the pit to the final product. Now clay can be delivered to railway trucks from the works in a matter of eight *hours* after the high-pressure monitor has prised it from the working face.

It is therefore important to preserve for posterity what little is left before it is too late. An example of how quickly an item of significance can be destroyed is seen in the blowing up at Goonbarrow on 13 January 1968 of the last (1912) stone-built engine house for a new Cornish beam engine. This engine, the last one to be made at the Charlestown Foundry in 1911, worked until 1932, and its bob can still be seen at East Pool where it was used as part of the surface balance-box for the giant 90in engine, now so important a technical monument that it is owned by the National Trust.

Of the great foundries that played their part in shaping the clay industry—St Austell established before 1816, St Blazey founded by William West in 1848, and Charlestown started in 1827—only the latter survives, now the foundry for English Clays (see pp 51-2).

Of the many china-stone grinding mills that abounded in the St Austell district, few remain today. The finest were the range of five mills in the Tregargus valley near St Stephen. At the head of the valley is the stone quarry and high above its floor was the first mill operated by a steel waterwheel, the water being pumped up from a well. The tailrace of this mill formed the headrace of the next below and so on down to the fourth mill. The last one is separated from the cluster of the upper four. The five overshot wheels varied from 22 to 35ft diameter and from 4ft 2in to 7ft breast; at least two were built by Bartle's Carn Brea Foundry in 1896 and in all they drove nineteen grinding pans (plate, p 89). These mills, operated by water engines, did not close down until about 1960, the last firm, Thomas Olver & Co Ltd, going into voluntary liquidation. Destruction began in the early winter of 1968 when the metal was sold to a scrap firm in Wales, but the Cornish Waterwheel Preservation Society, now merged with the Trevithick Society, saved one wheel at a cost of £350. If the conservation of industrial monuments had been taken far more seriously than it is, this site could have been made into a tourist attraction of specially high quality, quite apart from its educational value.

Sites of other china-stone mills are to be found at Wheelpit at the summit of the Carmears Incline, about half a mile due south-east of the Treffry Viaduct, where there was the original wheel (1840s) used to operate the Carmears railway inclined-plane. Chapel Mill, St Stephen ceased in 1953 and had a 21ft Charlestown Foundry wheel. In St Stephen Coombe, Coombe Mill had a 26ft Charlestown wheel, destroyed in May 1968. Other mills were at Wheal Arthur, St Stephen, Terras (which had an 1898 Bartle Carn Brea Foundry wheel), Trenoweth and Trevear, all in the St Stephen area. In another district altogether, but worthy of the record, there are sub-stantial remains of the Kergilliack stone-grinding mills owned by J. Lovering & Co in 1873 on the valley-side close by the Collegewood Viaduct at Penryn. The characteristic of these mills is the large waterwheel in the centre, the shafting running out on either side. The entire building was usually roofed over, but the wheel itself was open to the weather fore and aft.

Pont's Mill has a history going back nearly a century as a china-stone grinding-mill site. It lies at the northern end of the Treffry Canal, which linked it with Par Harbour and it was on Treffry's railway that ran from Par to Newquay. There were three mills: no 1 erected in 1874 was originally driven by a vertical spindle turbine, changed to an Escher Wyss turbine in 1903; no 2 was built in 1876 and a similar turbine was installed in 1904; no 3 mill, built in 1926, had another Escher Wyss turbine, driving 6 cylinder mills installed in 1959. The use of turbines at these mills was possible because of a high-level water supply giving a head of over 200ft, and the grinding was effected by the use of Chesil (Dorset) pebbles. They closed about 1967.

In 1943, the Cornish Engines Preservation Society in a report for the Institution of Mechanical Engineers, stated that there were twelve surviving beam engines recommended for preservation, six of which were in the St Austell district. Of these, only three survive intact in their engine houses. The first is the 50in engine built in 1863 for Penhalls Mine, then moved to Trevaunance Mine and in 1899 to Gooninnis Mine—all in St Agnes. In 1910, it was taken out and moved to the Goonvean clay works where it worked for about forty-five years. It is now owned by the Goonvean & Rostowrack China Clay Co and should certainly be preserved as a monument to Cornish engineering. The bob is a new one made by Holmans of Camborne in 1928, probably the last one ever to be made.

The second engine is at Parkandillack near St Dennis, built originally in 1852 by Sandys Vivian & Co at Copperhouse Foundry to a design by Thomas James, and erected at Trevaunance, St Agnes. At the venerable age of sixty, it was taken down, reconditioned by Bartle's Foundry at Carn Brea, and re-erected in a new engine house at the Parkandillack Clay Works where it worked for another forty-one years and was given the name 'Elizabeth'. In the engine house is the beginning of a collection of historical items used in the clay industry, and indeed this could well become an important museum. English Clays in 1970 restored this venerable engine and it now works by compressed air for historical purposes. (An engine originally at work in the St Austell district is the famous Rostowrack 22in engine, built by W. West in the St Blazey Foundry about 1850, now in the Holman Museum at Camborne where it works by compressed air.)

There is, however, a third engine still in its own house in the St Austell area that deserves special mention. It is the 30in at Greensplat clay works near Carthew and was the very last one to work in Cornwall, not ceasing until 22 February 1959. Its designer and maker are unknown—some say that it was St Blazey Foundry—and in a report in *The Cornishman* on 26 February 1959 commemorating its passing it was stated that it might be nearly 140 years old. It is owned by Berk Ltd of London, and it is just as important to preserve this historic machine as the remaining seven in the county.

With the introduction of the hydro-cyclone, and rapid methods of refining clay, micas are rapidly disappearing, although an excellent example is still to be seen at the Goonvean works, and where, too, the specialised tools of the industry can be seen still, eg the long-handle wooden 'shiver'. At Parkandillack pit, there still remain a set of micas and circular settling pits in which the 'button-hole launder' was used. This is a vertical hollow timber trough containing a number of plugs for draining the pit. To stand on the edge of the pit in cold weather, and take out one of these plugs 6 or 7ft down using long-handled tongs was no small feat, and one that could easily overbalance the operator!

The pans of the clay dries required special tiles for paving them—their thickness varies from $2\frac{1}{2}$ to 5in according to their nearness to the furnace—and a special tile (and brick) works was established at Carbis near Roche, at the western end of the branch line from Bugle. The clay was raised locally and brought by tramway to a kibbling mill worked by a 28ft waterwheel. After leaving the mill, the clay was transported by boys on a specially designed barrow having 'independent suspension' into a 'dry'. From here the tiles were taken into 'beehive kilns', their domes of Byzantine appearance, for firing. This interesting works met an untimely end one night in 1940. A zealous air-raid warden, seeing the glow of the kilns sent for the fire brigade, perhaps believing that a Nazi raid was imminent. The brigade did its work only too well for the works were put out of action never to recover! Today these special tiles are made at Wheal Remfry (185/ 925580).

The name of Charles Blondin (1824–97), who first walked across a 1,100ft long rope suspended 160ft above the Niagara Falls in 1859, is still remembered. At a later date, a transportation system was evolved in the Aberdeen Granite Quarries based on a suspended cable and called appropriately, the Blondin. At one time, there must have been many of these in operation in the Cornish granite and slate quarries, but the one still being used at Slip Chinastone Quarry, Goonvean is a rare survival. A sloping steel cable is slung across the top of the quarry, in this case a 'hole' in the ground nearly 250ft in depth, its ends securely anchored. On the floor of the quarry, the newly quarried stone is trammed to the picking-up point. The cable carries a two-wheeled trolley traversing its length, and underneath it is a pulley-block. The winding cable connects from the engine through the pulley and is fixed to a steel skip. The trolley runs down the fixed cable as the winding cable is paid out and when the skip is vertically above the picking-up point, it is dropped at high speed. As soon as the skip is loaded, the quarrymen signal to the engine-man, and it is hauled upwards to the pulley. The trolley is then pulled back by the winding cable carrying with it the skip and block until it reaches the engine house, close to which is the unloading point where the stone is released into waiting transport (plate, p 71).

On the west side of highway A391 (St Austell to Lanivet) at Carthew, are the clay mica-works known as Wheal Martyn (185/ 004555), which is probably the most historic example remaining of a small family business. The Martyn family purchased the Carthew Estate in 1790, and seven years later built their small family Georgian house. It was enlarged, no doubt as the family grew and their prosperity increased, in 1849. This clay works was managed in turn by Eliza, Richard, his widow and finally Miss Ivy Martyn before becoming part of the English China Clays 'empire'. It closed in 1966.

At the Wheal Martyn pit the clay, when raised, flowed as a slurry by gravity into a holding tank at the works. The only machine here was a 'water engine' which provided the power for pumping. A stream coming down the hillside from the west was diverted by launder to operate a large overshot wheel, 25ft diameter. By means of a crank, the revolving wheel induced horizontal motion into a 'flat-rod' about 100ft long. The other end of this rod is connected to a 'bob' pivoted on a fulcrum which converts horizontal motion into up-and-down motion; the other end of the bob is fixed to the vertical pumping rod (plates, pp 53–4). As the pump sucked up the slurry it discharged it into a set of micas from which the refined liquid gravitated down to settling tanks and finally to the kiln tanks located alongside the dry. As the water evaporated, the clay thickened and, when ready, a scoop was used to load trams with 'thin muck' or a shovel for 'thick muck' which deposited the clay direct to the pans. There it was spread and levelled by shiver, and then dried by coal firing for 12hr. It was then thrown out into the linhay on the opposite side of the dry. In all it took three months to condition the clay in the kiln tank before it was ready for panning.

This small intimate works, intact with all its constituent parts should be kept as a historic example of the industry. Not only can it be used for teaching, it could become a first-class tourist attraction. The water-engine described is a magnificent example of Cornish engineering skill in harnessing water-power for a clay-works pump. At one time there were hundreds of these ingenious engines in mines, quarries and clay works; this last one simply must not be destroyed. Nearby is a large 35ft diameter waterwheel that used to operate a flat-rod driving another pump 2,000ft away. It was rescued from oblivion in the late summer of 1968, and it too could become a part of the whole site. There can be no doubt at all of the historic value of this place, now over 170 years old.

The history of the clay industry in Cornwall is a part of the Cornish Renaissance of the century after 1760. In the race for more and more raw material, those who control it are exhorted not to destroy the comparatively few historic remnants which represent the archaeology of the men of clay, distinguished and undistinguished, common and uncommon, who laid the foundations of the now great industry of the latter half of this century.

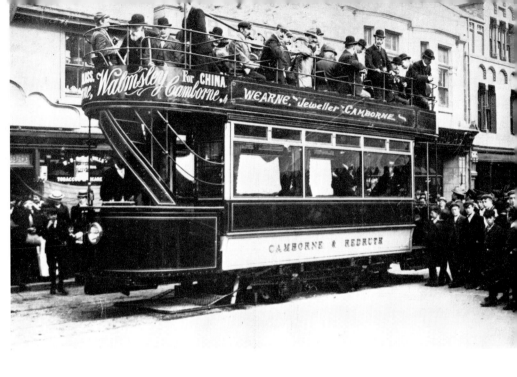

Page 125 (above) *The only tramline in Cornwall, between Camborne and Redruth, 1902–27. Photo taken at Commercial Square, Camborne;* (below) *Penzance harbour c1910. The Scilly steamer SS* Lyonesse, *Harvey-built at Hayle, 1889. Also showing the 1855 cast-iron lighthouse from Copperhouse Foundry, Hayle*

Page 126 (left) *St Pinnock viaduct in the Glynn Valley; 151ft high, the tallest in Cornwall, and designed by Brunel. The railway navvies raised these slate piers in 1854–5 for the Cornwall Railway. The original timber superstructure was replaced by the iron girders in 1882;* (below) *photograph taken about 1880 of the windmill on St Mary's, Scilly, the last operational one in 'Cornwall', built in 1820*

CHAPTER SEVEN

Communications

CANALS

WHEN Francis Egerton, 3rd Duke of Bridgewater, died in 1803 he had earned the title 'the father of British inland navigation'. Fifty-eight years before, Parliament had authorised the first modern canal, and Henry Berry, second of the great Liverpool Dock masters together with his surveyor John Eyes, constructed it. This was the Sankey (later St Helens) Canal from St Helens to Sankey Bridge near Warrington on the Mersey, constructed 1757–9 and it marked the start of the Canal Age.

During the forty years after 1765, 3,000 miles of man-made canals were added to 1,000 miles of rivers made navigable by new cuts, locks and weirs. When one thinks of the amount of finance raised from a public consisting of fewer than 9 million people in England and Wales in 1800; the fantastic quantity of labour recruited as navigators, who were known as 'navvies' from the 1790s onwards; the engineering achievements in the form of bridges, aqueducts, reservoirs, locks, pumping stations, houses for staff and thousands of barges; it is small wonder the period was called 'the Canal Mania'. Save for the building of the great cathedrals and monastic buildings in medieval England, Britain had seen nothing like it since the Romans had left. The vast navvy force, by sheer muscle power and horses, accomplished a new 'iron-age' architecture.

The industrial greatness of Britain during the latter half of the eighteenth century was built on her canal system and, in keeping with the momentous force of the Industrial Revolution that was just then beginning to exert itself, the prosperity of the canal companies was tremendous.

A Cornish family, the Praeds of Lelant played a significant part in this early canal-building activity. Their roots are deep in Cornish history. Kelly's *Directory* records, 'in Lelant church are memorials to the family of Praed 1620-1846', and Humphrey Mackworth Praed (b 1719) was Member of Parliament for St Ives and for Cornwall between 1761 and 1774. He almost entirely rebuilt Trevethow, his seat at Lelant, in 1761. He married Mary Forester and his son William was born in 1749. A banker in Truro and Falmouth, the latter founded Praeds Bank in London and followed his father into Parliament. He saw the great advantages of canals and, promoting the Grand Junction Canal Bill in 1790, he formed the company to build it. This great waterway from London to Birmingham, which totalled over 250 miles with all its branches, was a great achievement by a great Cornishman.

William Praed died at Trevethow in 1833, a man born at the beginning of the canal age and who lived to see the start of the railway age. He had married in 1778 Elizabeth Tyringham of Tyringham in North Buckinghamshire, and in the church of St Peter in the park there William's memorial reads:

> Sacred to the memory of William Praed and Elizabeth his wife. He was the son of Humphrey Mackworth Praed of Trevethow in Cornwall and through a long and active life was distinguished by a sound judgement and energy of character, ever alive to projects of local improvement and of great national importance. He represented the Borough of St Ives in several Parliaments and during that period contributed largely to the public good by the share he took in obtaining and carrying into effect the Act of Parliament for making and obtaining the Grand Junction Canal. His wife Elizabeth was the daughter and ultimately the sole heiress of Barnaby Backwell Esq, of Tyringham and the lineal descendant of the ancient family of Tyringham long settled in this county.

On the tablet is also a relief of a barge in a lock, so symbolic of canal engineering.

There is also another monument in Lelant churchyard. Another fitting memorial to William Praed is at the canal basin at Stoke Bruerne in Northamptonshire where there is now the unique Waterways Museum, recording the fascinating canal story over two centuries, housed in one of Praed's warehouses.

Cornish Canals

The traveller in Britain can still see much evidence of the canal works in the Midlands, where a new era has begun for them as waterways for leisure and recreation. Cornwall with its long coastline and facilities for shipping scarcely ever comes to mind in respect of canals, but they played a part in her industrial past.

The first we know about this was recorded in a report to the Penzance Natural History & Antiquarian Society by Mr H. M. Stocker in 1852 of a discovery of an underground canal at Carclase tin mine 'which had not been seen for at least 120 years'. It was a tunnel about half a mile long and when discovered by mining operations there were flat-bottomed barges 6ft long. It is ascribed to a Mr Parnall. The report itself is interesting as an early example of industrial archaeology.

Another Cornishman interested in canal projects in his native county was John Edyvean of St Austell, whom the *Monthly Review* in the 1770s described as 'a man who dissipated his wealth in pursuits that had for their object the good of mankind'—in 1777 he proposed a scheme for a canal to traverse the entire kingdom! In 1774 Dr Campbell's *Political Survey of Britain* advocated the building of a canal at Bude and in that year John Edyvean mooted a project to link Bude Haven—the present town was virtually non-existent—with the Tamar at Calstock by a canal 90 miles long. The previous year, Edyvean had promoted an act to build a canal in the Newquay district, of which two stretches were accomplished, for details of which see Newquay in Gazetteer. Over almost two centuries, time has obliterated a great deal of this early canal venture, but reference to the first 25in Ordnance Survey maps of Cornwall, made a century after the work was completed, and a field excursion, will prove its existence.

The famous Cornish philosopher and historian the Rev Dr William Borlase (1695–1772) also put forward a canal project to connect the River Camel at Polbrock, midway between Bodmin and Wadebridge, with the Fowey River, Polbrock being navigable from Padstow. This was a project that lingered on, John Rennie being called in at one stage, but it came to nothing and was finally superseded by the Bodmin & Wadebridge Railway in the 1830s. Other Cornish canal ideas that came to naught were the navigation from Gweek to St Erth, designed by the Irish-American Robert Fulton in the 1790s and another from Hayle to Carwynnen near Camborne in 1801, both associated with transport to and from metal mines. A project put forward by Silas Martin of Crantock two decades later was another case in point. This was to have been a canal to transport lead ore from the Old Wheal Rose, Newlyn East, to the Gannel, with a branch to Retyn near Indian Queens to take beach-sand inland for fertilising.

Shelly-sand was much in demand by Cornish farmers in the eighteenth century for use as a soil conditioner since its calcium content made it an alternative to lime. It was written of Bude Haven, for instance, that the bright yellow sand, composed of shells, had been used for a long time as a manure, ie fertiliser. In G. B. Worgan's *General View of the Agriculture of Cornwall* (1811) it was recorded that packhorse trains took sand miles inland, and Murray's *Handbook for Travellers in Devon and Cornwall* (1865) stated that 'at low water this Bude Haven bay is a scene of considerable bustle since it supplies the neighbouring parts of Devon and Cornwall with sea-sand, carried up the country in such amazing quantities that 4,000 horse-loads have been taken from the shore in a single day'. It was this sand that brought about Cornwall's longest canal scheme that came to fruition during the reign of George IV.

The first scheme had been mooted nearly half a century before, gaining the support of the Molesworth family who had been concerned with civic affairs in Cornwall as well as with agricultural improvements on their estates. But it was not until Lord Stanhope, the father of Lady Hester Stanhope, and who owned an estate at

Holsworthy, took an active interest that the canal came to fruition. Construction began in July 1819 and it opened four years later, using tub-boats 20ft × 5½ft × 20in carrying 5 tons.

From an embankment at Bude Haven constructed in a manner similar to Plymouth Breakwater, a sea lock effected entrance into a basin available for coastal vessels up to about 120 tons, bringing in coal from South Wales, timber and salt, and exporting agricultural produce and bark for tanning. The lock and basin were enlarged in 1836 and 1856. The widest part of the canal, from this basin up to Hele (Heyl) Bridge, Marhamchurch, where the remains of a wharf still exists, is visible today. From here the canal ran up the valley to Redpost, with two inclined planes: one over 800ft long rising 120ft at Marhamchurch and operated by a 50ft waterwheel; and the other and more famous one at Hobbacott Down, 935ft long and rising 225ft with a gradient of 1 in 4. From Redpost, at the junction of A3072 with B3254 the canal ran northwards to terminate at the reservoir, holding 195 million gallons of water, near Alfardisworthy, 450ft above sea level and covering 70 acres. Today it is known as the Tamar Lake and after the demise of the canal in the 1890s (it carried 30,000 tons of sand as late as 1888) it became the water supply source for Bude and district. *The Times* reported in October 1968 that, as it was being replaced as a water source by the North Devon Water Board, it may be developed as a wild life reserve by the Devon Trust for Nature Conservation. It is partly in Cornwall, partly in Devon. From Redpost, the southern branch of this canal ran down to Tamerton Bridge, and in 1825 was extended to Druxton 3 miles north-east of Launceston. The act authorised nearly 50 miles of which about 35 were built.

The Hobbacott plane was the most notable engineering achievement on the canal and the longest plane built on any tub-boat canal. Murray's *Handbook for Travellers* (1865) recorded:

It is an ingenious substitute for a chain of locks and consists of a steep roadway, about 900 feet in length, furnished with two lines of rails dipping at each end into the canal, and traversed by an endless chain. The barges, which are provided with small iron wheels, and generally loaded with sand, are raised or lowered on this roadway by being attached to the chain, which is set in motion by two enormous buckets, each 8ft in diameter, alternately filled with water and working in wells 225 feet in depth. As soon as the descending bucket has reached the bottom of the well, it strikes upon a stake which raises a plug, when the water runs out in one minute and finds its way out through an adit to the canal below. This bucket is then in readiness to be raised by the other, which, having been filled with water, descends in its turn. A steam engine is also at hand should the buckets become unserviceable.

There were six of these planes on this canal.

Today, one can see the outline of the Hobbacott plane from Coombepark Farm, on the hillside and clearly marked by two hedges. At the head of the incline, the basin is empty and grass-grown, to the north of it is a shallow cliff. Here is the stone-built engine house and, below it, the single-storey house where the incline-keeper lived—a windswept place facing south-west. It must have been a lonely existence here for his family and a hard enough job for the keeper. Charles Hadfield, the canal historian, has recorded that on a mid-summer day in 1827 '59 boats were taken over the plane' and for this the wage was of the order of about a florin (10p) a day.

The 1770s was a period of much canal promotion in Cornwall for yet another was promoted, the Looe Union Canal from Looe up the valley to Liskeard; but it was not opened until 1828. With its northern terminal basin at Moorswater in the valley below Liskeard, it was built at a cost of £17,200 by the engineer Robert Coad to take agricultural produce and stone from the Cheesewring quarries down to the sea and to bring in coal, iron, timber, and merchandise for Liskeard, as well as limestone and culm to be burned at kilns at Moorswater, the remains of two of which can still be seen. It became an important link for the copper-mining industry (p 41). With the building of the railway to Looe in 1859–60, the canal was virtually abandoned although it was used up to about 1909. Today one can still see some remains: derelict locks, cuts and bridges, particularly the section alongside the railway station at St Keyne.

The other small canal in Cornwall, parts of which are still to be seen, is the Par Canal, the 2 miles of navigation built by the mining promoter Joseph Treffry of Fowey. Opened in 1847 it ran from Par harbour to a basin at Pont's Mill near Tywardreath Highway. There was one lock and the canal was much used for the transport of copper ore from the Fowey Consolidated Mines as well as for china-stone.

A Cornish canal project from the earliest days of the canal era was at Copperhouse Pool, Hayle; a description appears in Chapter Five.

RAILWAY DEVELOPMENT 1809–1908

The ever growing pace of the new industrial age after 1750 brought about an enormous amount of railway building throughout the nine-teenth century. The great strides made in iron smelting, in the production of engines and in the development of steam power led to the steam locomotive, and the plaque erected by the Birmingham engineering firm of Tangye Brothers (founded by five Cornishmen from Illogan in 1864) on the building in Cross Street, Redruth, records that 'here lived William Murdock (1754–1839) who made the first locomotive here and tested it in 1784'. Eight years later, Mur-doch, in this building, was the first to demonstrate in Cornwall the use of coal gas for illumination (see p 187), and Cornwall can claim that it pioneered the gas industry and the steam locomotive in consequence.

The great Cornishman, Richard Trevithick, born at Carn Brea 1771, was associated with the Darby foundry at Coalbrookdale in Shropshire during the last decade of the eighteenth century, and Dr Arthur Raistrick has recently proved that it was here in 1802 that the first successful trial locomotive ran on rails (Murdoch's was only a model). It was designed by Trevithick, who inaugurated the era of high-pressure steam in 1801.

Late in the 1790s a tramroad had been constructed by the Glamor-gan Canal Co to afford a transport link between the Pen-y-darren and Dowlais Ironworks and the canal at Abercynon. On 21 February

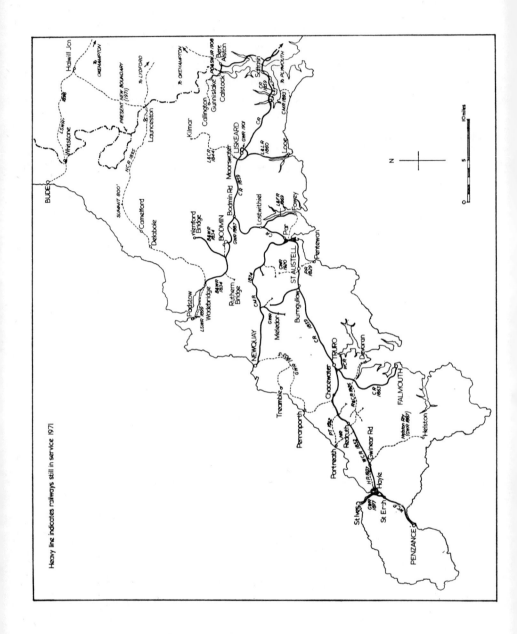

Heavy line indicates railways still in service 1971

1804, Trevithick's locomotive successfully hauled 10 tons of iron and 70 men a distance of almost 10 miles on this railway. Trevithick remarked: 'It was the first self-moving machine managed by one man.'

The Bodmin & Wadebridge Railway

The first railways to come to Cornwall to transport produce from mines were, however, tramroads using horses as motive power. But, following royal assent in 1832, an important milestone in transport was achieved with the Bodmin & Wadebridge Railway, the first in Cornwall to use steam. In 1792, Robert Fox, Peter Price and Joseph Tregelles of Falmouth (who were amongst those who had started the Perran Foundry the previous year) leased the Neath Abbey Iron Works in South Wales. In 1833 the Bodmin & Wadebridge directors ordered from this foundry their first locomotive and 4 July 1834 should be recorded as a red-letter day in Cornish railway history. On that day, this engine designed by a Cornishman Henry Taylor, appropriately called *Camel*, made her first trial trip from Wadebridge to be followed on 15 July by the first-ever passenger train, although the line was not opened officially until Michaelmas. The railway, purchased by the LSWR in 1846, remained quite isolated until the GWR linked it with their Bodmin station in 1887 but it was not joined to the LSWR main line until the North Cornwall Railway reached Wadebridge in 1895. The B&W not only ran between those towns, it had a long branch up the Camel Valley to Wenford Bridge.

Today, the freight line that runs from Boscarne Junction to Wenford, serving the Wenford clay dries and winding up the picturesque valley, is the most northerly point of the railway system in Cornwall. At the Wenford terminus can be seen the iron chairs that carry the rails marked 'L & SWR 1887'. If this line ceases for freight could it not become Cornwall's 'Bluebell line' with memories of those far-off days when the first train of passengers came to Wenford on 30 September 1834, or of that golden period when hundreds of tons of granite were taken every year from the De Lank Quarries by railway over this line for shipment to many parts of the world? (plate, p 54).

The Great Western Railway

The most important railway to be built in Cornwall was the 75 miles from Saltash to Penzance. Its antecedents in the west lay in the Hayle Railway, details of which are to be found in the chapter on Hayle and which first opened just before Christmas 1837. The building of the through line was by two companies, the Cornwall and the West Cornwall and the works took the twelve years 1847–59 to complete, all under the direction of Isambard Brunel. The first sod was cut at Burngullow, west of St Austell, in 1847.

The Royal Albert Bridge at Saltash, used for the first train to Truro on 11 April 1859, was described in Murray's *Handbook for Travellers*:

> This extraordinary viaduct, which for novelty and ingenuity of construction, stands unrivalled in the world, carries the new railroad at a height of 100 feet above the water on 19 spans or arches of which two alone bridge the estuary in gigantic leaps of 455 feet by means of Mr Brunel's ingenious combination of arch, tubular girder and suspension chain.

The great flat iron links of these chains, numbering about 1,150, were originally made by the Cornish foundrymen at Copperhouse for Brunel's great 700ft span suspension bridge at Clifton early in the 1850s. The bridge did not materialise, however, until after Brunel's death (it was opened in 1864) and he purchased the Clifton Bridge chains for the Cornwall Railway. They were brought back to Copperhouse and then used for Saltash. In 1968 it was stated by British Rail that this great bridge, the greatest structural engineering achievement of the Cornwall, later GWR, which took over the railway in 1876, is still good for another twenty-five years.

This railway, a magnificent example of Victorian engineering, is characterised by its many viaducts, all of them originally built partly of timber. A few on the line between Saltash and St Germans via Earth (abandoned in 1908) had to be built entirely of timber, but the others were of the timber 'fan' type. They were so well built that eight of them on the Falmouth branch constructed in 1861–2 lasted until between 1927 and 1934, the last one, at Collegewood, Penryn, being superseded by a masonry viaduct in July 1934. The last Victorian viaduct of all to be rebuilt, Trenance at Newquay, was completed in August 1939, the original timber bridge having been rebuilt in stone with iron girders in 1874. To this day, in a number of cases where a new viaduct was built alongside the old one, the original stone piers—the archaeological remains of the railway builders—still stand.

Throughout many other districts in Cornwall, branch lines were built from small towns to link with the main line. There was the Looe to Moorswater for Liskeard, with the Moorswater–Liskeard link (1901) that falls 210ft from the main-line station down into the valley at Coombe, the steepest gradient in Cornwall, 1 in 35·4. The railway first came into Launceston from Tavistock in 1865; Fowey joined up with Lostwithiel in 1869 (later to be closed and then reopened in 1895 by the GWR); and in the 1870s the last 7ft broad-gauge line to be built in Britain, the 4¼ mile branch from St Ives Road (now St Erth) to St Ives. Helston, after many years of trying, was finally linked to the main line at Gwinear Road in 1887. Bodmin to Bodmin Road came in the same year and then, in the early twentieth century, the lure of the 'Cornish Riviera' beaches and the new industry of tourism brought about the Chacewater to Perranporth and Newquay branch 1903–5. The last railway of all was the line from Callington (Kelly Bray) to Bere Alston in Devon via Calstock, over the graceful Calstock Viaduct, opened in 1908 and operated by the Plymouth, Devonport & South Western Junction Railway.

Two interesting buildings in the severe functional tradition of industrial architecture should be noted. At Lostwithiel there is the carriage works of the Cornwall Railway built in 1858. It is situated on the north side of the main line to the west of the station and is constructed of 'killas'—a yellowy-brown slate—with ranges of round-arched windows with yellow brick dressings. The second structure is the large red-brick district branch building, 500ft long, that Sir Moreton Peto (1809–89) constructed for the Cornwall Minerals Railway at St Blazey in the years 1872–4. Peto was a highly successful railway builder and he built part of the GWR in Middlesex and Buckinghamshire in the 1830s.

Station buildings worthy of note are Saltash, St Germans and Lostwithiel c 1854–7; Penzance as rebuilt by the GWR in 1879, soon after it took possession of the WCR; and the goods shed at Penryn of 1862, which is a simple rectangular structure of local stone with slate roof, roofed with large queen-post timber trusses and internally all the wall surfaces and roof timbers lime-washed.

The LSWR, afterwards the Southern Railway

There is one more story of Cornish railway history to relate, of a line—the 'South-Western' that has now become almost wholly a part of her industrial archaeology. For years the inhabitants of North Cornwall had waited patiently for a railway but its sparse population, very small towns and little industry offered scant reward to railway promoters. The LSWR, ever-enterprising, was pushing its tracks into the remoter parts of north-west Devon and its navvies had reached Halwill Junction, about 7 miles from the Cornish border, at the end of January 1879. The north Cornishmen felt that here was their opportunity and the North Cornwall Railway Company (an LSWR subsidiary) was formed in 1882–3. Money was tight and the first train did not arrive in Launceston from Halwill until summer 1886. Then began the long years of railway building by the NCR, engineered by an Okehampton man called Stinchcombe, his navvies toiling across the bleak moors and over the 800ft summit near Hendraburnick (174/117875) to reach Camelford in August 1893. Wadebridge was finally reached in 1895 when the old and ancient Bodmin & Wadebridge Railway was joined to its owners after nearly fifty years. This line must surely have been gruelling work in the winter particularly at the time of the Great Blizzard of 1891. The terminus of the line was reached in March 1899 when the 5½ miles was opened from Wadebridge to Padstow and the previous year the LSWR itself had reached the Atlantic coast at Bude from Holsworthy.

Ninety years after the opening of the Poldice Tramway in West Cornwall, it was now possible to reach the coast of North Cornwall at Padstow direct from Waterloo, a distance of 260 miles. This achievement was to bring about in 1927 the advent of the Atlantic Coast Express. S. P. B. Mais wrote in the 1930s about this line:

> We climb out of Launceston into a very different land, through Egloskerry and Tresmeer with rhododendrons growing on the station platforms. Then on to the open moor to get a wide view of the Atlantic beyond. This is nearer the Ireland of Connemara and over the bogs rise the eerie rocky tors of Brown Willy and Rough Tor. At Padstow the Southern Railway reached the Atlantic and the nearest land is in another hemisphere, 3,000 miles away.

Today all is gone forever. No more is seen and heard the sound of the Victorian T9 engines that were a particular feature of this line until 1962, or the great Bulleid Pacifics on the Atlantic Coast Express. No more will trains traverse the only railway tunnel in North Cornwall at Trelill that the navvies blasted through in 1895. Bude station, built of red-brick and reminiscent of London suburbia and from whence the last-ever steam train in Cornwall departed for Holsworthy on 5 September 1965, has been demolished. The last passenger trains on these very late Victorian lines ran on 1 October 1966 from Launceston to Wadebridge, and from Bodmin Road to Padstow on 31 January 1967.

HARBOURS

Cornwall has the longest coast-line by far of any county in England and Wales, 321 miles measured on the 1in map, and the long narrow peninsula had over forty harbours testifying to her coastal trade and her concern with ships over many generations. Harbours that are particularly concerned with mining and quarrying can be split up into three groups: the south coast, the Penwith peninsula and the north coast.

Starting in the south, Looe is an old refuge where the prosperity
arising from the metal mining and quarrying high up in the hills
around Caradon brought about new quays built in the middle of the
nineteenth century. These were connected first by canal to Liskeard
in 1828 and then to the southern terminus of the Liskeard & Caradon
Railway opened in 1844. To the east of this once important mining
area was the Tamar Valley and so prolific were its mines and quarries
that the ore and the granite trade overloaded that railway and canal
system to the south, so that some of the trade had to be diverted
overland to the quays at Calstock on the Tamar which saw considerable activity in the nineteenth century. Here the East Cornwall
Minerals Railway came from Kelly Bray in 1872 and later on the
unusual steam-powered lift that raised a 15 ton wagon up 113ft from
the quay to the level of the railway at the north end of the Calstock
Viaduct (see Calstock in Gazetteer).

The development of the china-clay industry brought about the
development of Fowey as a china-clay port with its deep-water berths
for ships larger than those that could use Par. Eight special jetties
were constructed after 1870 for handling clay, china-stone and coal;
an enterprise much associated with the Great Western Railway and
completed in 1923. The other ports on the south coast particularly
associated with the clay industry are Par, Charlestown and Pentewan,
details of which are to be found in Chapter Six.

Around the Lizard peninsula are three small ports. Gweek at the
head of the Helford River is a small port to which coastal ships still
come bringing coal, and there is some evidence that ships from the
Mediterranean called here for tin twenty centuries ago. In medieval
times, Gweek had a thriving trade with Scandinavia. The other two
industrial 'ports of call' are the piers at Porthoustock and at Dean
Point, used by ships calling for crushed 'blue elvan' produced at two
quarries. Dean Point, an old pier, was reopened in the later 1940s:
the old pier at Porthoustock on the north side of the cove was constructed about 1895 and last used in December 1958 (plate, p 89).

Around the Penwith peninsula, Porthleven witnessed the building of a new harbour 1812–16 and in 1854 the important Harvey family of Hayle, then in its heyday, purchased it and extended its docks. Ships brought in coal, timber and limestone for agriculture and the ore from local mines was sent away to smelters. China clay was also exported until 1916. Three-masted schooners from Norway frequently came here for mackerel and an ice-works was constructed. It is now enjoying a revival of boat-building.

In the middle of the nineteenth century, Lamorna (see also p 169) was the port from which granite was shipped. The pier was built about 1853–4.

The story of the port of Hayle, so much concerned with the prosperity of Cornwall between 1770 and 1900, is found in Chapter Five. It was with Hayle that the first railway in West Cornwall connected that other mining port, Portreath, in 1838. Portreath, formerly Bassett's Cove, was developed after 1760 by a 'company of adventurers' who included the Fox family of Falmouth and who had taken a lease from Francis Bassett of Tehidy. A pier, warehouses and jetty were built costing £13,000, extended between 1778 and 1781 and further extensions were made in later years. It continued to be used for the importing of coal from South Wales until October 1960.

The last group of mining and quarrying ports are the north-coast ports between St Agnes and Bude. St Agnes is a story of disaster from the sea. A pier, probably associated with mining, is recorded in 1632 at Trevaunance Porth: Henry Winstanley (of Eddystone fame) built another 1699–1705, and a third was built in 1710. The mining prosperity brought about a new harbour in the 1790s at a cost of £30,000 and ships bringing in Welsh coal and taking away ore used it until 1915. The following year it was overwhelmed by the sea. Ships lay underneath the cliff and cargo was hauled upwards from their holds by a horse-whim mounted on a wide ledge high above.

The history of the recent harbour at Newquay is found in Chapter Two but it is worthy of note that a *Cartulary* of Bishop Lacey of Exeter mentions 'NEW KAYE' in 1439. Between 1839 and 1881 there was a thriving shipbuilding industry here, thirty-nine ships being

built, the largest the schooner *Mary Peers* of 230 tons. The demise of
Newquay harbour lies in section 60 of the GWR Act 1929—'Newquay
Harbour is abandoned herewith!'

In the extreme north of Cornwall are a number of small refuges,
four of which owed some of their importance to slate quarrying: Port
William, Port Isaac, Port Gaverne and Boscastle. Prior to the opening
of the North Cornwall Railway to Delabole in 1893, these small
places had a thriving slate trade, horse-drawn carts bringing great
quantities of slate for shipment in 60ft Appledore and Bideford
ketches and smacks. Three of them were the *Teazer*, the *Telephone*
and the *Telegraph*. Coal, lime and grain were imported, but trading
ceased half a century ago. At Boscastle, an inlet like a miniature
fjord, the smacks were rowed in by eight-oared gigs. The most
northerly of all the harbours in Cornwall is Bude and details of its
history are found earlier in this chapter.

Between Plymouth and Land's End are eight harbours that have
probably owed their origin and development to the basic industry of
fishing. Polperro is an old port where the Duchy of Cornwall celebrated the Diamond Jubilee of 1897 by erecting a new pier. Mevagissey has been long associated with fishing since it paid £485 in
tithe for fish landed in 1769 and its piers were rebuilt 1770–3. As the
china-clay trade which once used this port moved eastwards to
Charlestown and Par, the fishing industry increased to such an extent
that £22,000 was spent on a new harbour 1888–90 enclosing 14 acres
of water. The great blizzard in March 1891 destroyed it all and a new
harbour was built in 1897 at a cost of £32,000.

Portscatho, Coverack, Mullion and Sennen are all small fishing
harbours, Mousehole is mentioned in records of the time of King
John. Its old quay was built in the 1390s, extended early in the
eighteenth century, and a reflection of its nineteenth-century prosperity is the expenditure of £5,000 in 1870–1 for the new north pier,
designed by William Tregarthen Douglass in 1869, erected by the
granite-quarrying firm of Freeman & Sons. R. J. Roddis in his book
Cornish Harbours stated that Lerryn 'long in decay at the head of the

Page 143 Delabole slate quarry about 1875 showing the western face, incline, waterwheel operating a Cornish 'lift' to the right of the incline, and papote head at top centre

Page 144   *Undershot paddle wheel at Hingham corn mill, Egloshayle, near Wadebridge—one of the very few mills working in Cornwall*

Fowey estuary, only rarely saw an occasional coal barge', but its trade had ceased by 1939. St Mawes is a small harbour where the pier was built by a local company under an act of 1854, destroyed by the sea eighteen years later and rebuilt in 1873. Another harbour of great antiquity is St Michael's Mount which William Morton the chaplain constructed c 1428. Passing from the ownership of the church in 1540, the Mount went first to the Arundell family, then to the Bassetts and finally to the St Aubyns in 1657. A local entrepreneur George Blewett of Marazion (1688–1766) built part of the present harbour in 1725 and further extensions were made in 1823–4 by the St Aubyns.

The notable engineer John Smeaton designed the new harbour at St Ives in 1767 at a cost of £10,000 and in 1816 a breakwater was commenced but abandoned after an outlay of £30,000. It was part of a project concerned with the creation of a harbour of refuge for St Ives. Smeaton's harbour was lengthened in 1888–94 and a new south pier built. Like so many other small Cornish ports, the trade has gone, and the last collier to call was in 1935. The remains of the railway for the crane on Smeaton's pier are extant.

In 1836, Augustus John Smith, a Hertfordshire landowner, took a lease of the Scillies from the Duchy of Cornwall, under which there was an obligation to complete the rebuilding of Hugh Town pier. It was finished in 1838 and extended in 1889. Its importance today is that it is the only harbour for the sea-link with the mainland.

Evidence of the longevity of the port of Newlyn is provided by the fact that the people appealed to the Bishop of Exeter in 1435 for money to rebuild their 'KAY'; the little jetty is still in existence. The curiously named Rev Wladislaw Somerville Lach-Szyrma, Vicar of Newlyn in the 1880s, launched an appeal in 1881 which resulted in the construction of what has become the largest fishing port in the south-west.* Forty acres of water are enclosed by the North Arm, built between 1884–94 and the South Pier completed 1886, now used by coasters of many nations loading crushed stone and tarmacadam from the nearby Penlee Quarry. The pier is connected with the quarry

* Designed by James Inglis, who became Chief Engineer to the GWR in 1892

I

by a small 24in gauge railway, the most westerly in England, and the stone is taken even as far afield as Lübeck on the Baltic.

The final group of harbours are those associated with six towns, Truro, Penryn, Falmouth, Penzance, Padstow and Wadebridge. Long before the railway came to Truro in 1852, its quays were busy with shipping and merchandise and an early photograph shows the main town quay, with its single-arched bridge at the foot of Lemon Street. The present extensive Lemon Quay car park was then a part of Truro Harbour. In 1939 the port handled 57,000 tons of imports and its maritime history is visible in several old warehouses on the north-east bank of the river near Boscawen Quay. They are probably of late eighteenth-century date. During World War II, Truro handled 100,000 tons of shipping in 1944, but a few years after the war the tonnage had dropped to less than a tenth of that figure.

The wharves of the port of Penryn, up to the mid-1930s, were piled with granite blocks, lorries rumbling down from the Mabe quarries, and there was a considerable shipborne stone trade. It has had a long history as a port, long before the new town of Falmouth came into being at the time of the Restoration, and it exported the produce of the mines in the seventeenth century. Reference to the 1878 Ordnance Survey shows several industries located near to its quays: iron foundries, tanyards, a papermill, granite works, manure manufactory and a saw mill. All of them have gone, but the quays still provide moorings for small coastal ships bringing in coal.

Two miles down river lies Falmouth, a small hamlet called Smithicke four centuries ago, when Pendennis Castle was built by order of King Henry VIII (1542–6). The building of this castle and that of St Mawes on the eastern side of the Roads (1540–3) was a part of the national coast-defence programme, and both testify to the importance of this anchorage. Falmouth came into being under a charter of King Charles II in August 1660 and twenty-eight years later it became a government mail packet station which service lasted until 1852. A memorial of 1898 to the memory of the 'Gallant Officers and Men' of the packet ships is to be seen at The Moor opposite the

General Post Office. The prosperity of the port brought about the building of a new harbour in 1705, the historian Leland speaking of it as 'a haven noteable and famous'. In 1859–60 the docks were built by the firm of Cox Farley covering an area of 120 acres, with a tidal harbour of 42 acres, with extensive facilities for ship repairing. The first ship entered the new docks on 10 July 1861. A further pier, the Prince of Wales, was opened in May 1905. One of the last great sailing ships of the Australian grain fleet, the Finnish barquentine *Passant* called at Falmouth in 1939. Steam locomotives still haul trains in the docks, and with the two at Par Docks, are now (1971) the only steam railway engines in general use in Cornwall.

Among the early records of the port of Penzance is one of 1337 showing that the rent paid to the 'Duchy Havener' by the town was 12s (60p) as compared with a figure of £5 for Mousehole and £1 for Newlyn; but Penzance undoubtedly had a quay, since the public records disclose that in the early fifteenth century ships from the town were licensed to carry pilgrims to Spain. Henry VIII in 1512 granted the town the right to collect harbour dues (keelage and bushellage) on condition that the quays were kept in good repair. The increasing tin trade was responsible for the rebuilding of the quay in 1745, extensions being made later on in that century, again in 1812 and then by the building of the Albert Pier completed in 1853, the year after the opening of the West Cornwall Railway to Truro. The entry of the first steamship into the harbour was in 1825, and 1884 saw the opening of the new floating dock adjoining the depot of Trinity House then recently established. Next to it is Holman's dry dock (1879–80).

A century ago, Murray's *Handbook* described Padstow as 'one of those antiquated unsavoury fishing towns which are viewed more agreeably from a distance!' Its royal charter had been granted in 1583, and long before this there came pilgrims making their pilgrimage to the shrine of St Petroc. As early as the seventeenth century, copper ore was sent from here to Swansea smelters. In 1842 the paddle steamer *Brilliant* owned by Vivian Stephens of St Ives began a regular run from that harbour to Bristol, calling at Padstow three times a month for North Cornish passengers. This may well have been a contributory factor in the deepening of the harbour and rebuilding of the pier in 1854, following an act of 1844 for improving the port. To the harbour came the LSWR in March 1899, the last new railway to be built in Cornwall in the nineteenth century and that company further developed the harbour facilities. A new north jetty was built and the commissioners' pier extended in 1934. Padstow's fishing fleet numbered 151 in 1912. Wadebridge has been an important port in its day but all maritime trade ceased in 1962.

LIGHTHOUSES

Cornish Mainland

No survey of Cornish harbours, however brief, would be complete without a reference to the building of the lighthouses on and around the coastline, since they are a part of the long maritime history of Britain.

The first to be described is the lighthouse on the Plymouth Breakwater, a mile off the coast at Picklecombe Point, Cawsand, whose keepers used to be enumerated in the Cornwall Census in the nineteenth century, as is shown by the Cornwall Register for 1847.

The Breakwater, a mammoth engineering feat with which Richard Trevithick was associated, was started in 1812 and was finally completed in 1845. Eight years earlier Sir John Rennie had put forward the proposal to erect the lighthouse, and the granite was obtained from the quarries at Luxulyan. It is 74ft to the top, 18ft diameter and was completed in 1844. Its designer was James Walker.

Thirteen miles to the south-west and the same distance due south of the Cornish coast lies the Eddystone reef. The first lighthouse was completed in November 1698, constructed of timber by Henry Winstanley of Saffron Walden. After its first winter it was strengthened with stone and considerably rebuilt by Winstanley to a height of 60ft: the earlier one was 35ft high. This tower was completely swept away with its keepers and its creator during a furious gale on the night of

26–7 November 1703. A Cornishman, John Rudyard, built the third tower completed in 1709, but this was destroyed by fire in 1755. This was followed by the first great 'rock lighthouse' of John Smeaton FRS (1724–92). Built of De Lank granite from St Breward, this famous tower lasted until 1882, to be followed by the present one, also built of the same stone. The upper part of Smeaton's first tower was re-erected as a memorial to its designer on Plymouth Hoe where it still stands.

Between Rame Head and Land's End are six lighthouses, the first a Georgian building, originally called the Falmouth Light and now St Anthony. Built by a Mr Olver of Falmouth it was first lit in April 1835 and was designed by the same James Walker who was responsible for the light on Plymouth Breakwater.

The original Lizard light was in use between 1619 and 1630. It failed because of lack of finance to support it. The light tower that still exists today is one of two originally constructed by Thomas Fonnereau in 1752. Originally they carried coal-fired beacons, altered to oil-lamps then to carbon-arc lamps and filament lamps, mains electricity coming in 1950. Here there are the beginnings of a museum of lighthouse archaeology, including a nineteenth-century 'caloric engine' used in lighthouses for generating electricity, and the original 'magneto machine' installed at the Lizard in 1878.

There are two small harbour lights at Penzance and Newlyn. The former is supported on a cast-iron Doric column, designed by John Matthews the then Borough Surveyor of Penzance, and made by the Copperhouse Foundry in 1855: the latter, made by Butler Bros of Smethwick in 1914, is at the end of the South Pier.

The dangerous coast westwards from Newlyn brought about the erection of the Tater-Du light first lit in July 1965—the newest of all those maintained by the Trinity House depot at Penzance. Although this light itself is not yet industrial archaeology, it was at the site of this depot in 1861 that the work-yard was established for the making of the lighthouse on the Wolf Rock to the design of James Walker and, after his death, of James Douglass, afterwards Sir James Douglass, Engineer-in-Chief, Trinity House, from 1862. For seven years an average of seventy men worked on the reef, often in appalling conditions, and nearly 4,500 tons of Lamorna granite were shipped out from Penzance. It was an epic story exemplifying Victorian determination. The light celebrated its centenary on 1 January 1970.

The first light on the Longships reef off Land's End was displayed in 1795 and it lasted until 1873 when it was replaced by the present tower built partly of Cornish granite and partly (curiously enough) of stone imported from Dinant in France. At St Ives, long after the completion of the harbour by John Smeaton in 1768, a stone light-house was built in 1830 on the pier and was lit by gas when the town gas works was established in 1835. It was replaced in 1890 by an iron tower made by Stothert & Pitt of Bath on the extension to the pier.

Across St Ives Bay is the island of Godrevy. Its lighthouse was built in 1859 after two centuries of shipwrecks culminating in the foundering of the *Nile*, belonging to the Irish Steamship Co, in December 1854 with considerable loss of life. It was another James Walker design, built by Eva & Williams of Helston.

The two remaining lighthouses on the mainland are those at Pendeen and Trevose. The former is described by Trinity House as 'a typical shore-station with light and separate accommodation for three keepers and their families'. It was completed in 1900. The other is on Trevose Head, Padstow, originally proposed in 1809 but not started until 1845 and first lit in December 1847. It has a fog signal of 'eight great trumpets'.

Scilly Isles

Over the lintel of a door on a tower in St Agnes, Scilly, is an inscription 'Erected by Capt Hugh Till and Capt Symon Bayly 1680'. This is one of the oldest lighthouses in Britain and it served shipping for 231 years, not being extinguished until 1911 when it was replaced by a new one on Peninnis Head, St Mary's. The St Agnes light was built by Trinity House, a tower of 51ft with a windlass for raising the coal and a chute for discharging the ashes. The coal-fired beacon was replaced by an Argand oil-lamp in 1790 with a silvered-copper reflector having a visibility of 18 miles.

On Round Island in the extreme north of the Scilly archipelago a lighthouse was built in 1887 to the design of William Tregarthen Douglass, son of Sir James; this is still extant.

The 15 April 1847 saw the sailing from Penzance of a Trinity House steamer equipped to start the erection of a curious iron lighthouse, resembling an early Victorian water-tower supported on six columns, to be built on the Bishop Rock, but a great gale blew it away in 1850. Trinity House then set about designing a granite rock tower and this was finished by September 1858 to the design of James Walker. It was strengthened in 1874 and, following the completion of the present Eddystone light in 1882, the equipment came westward and the Bishop was virtually rebuilt in the next five years in the charge of William Tregarthen Douglass. It stands, isolated, 4 miles out from the western shores of St Agnes and is the first landfall for ships entering the English Channel. The men who built it during the 1850s lived in the summer months in a camp on the rocky islet of Rosvear, 2 miles to the east, and it was a heroic achievement. A plaque on the tower commemorates all who took part and ends with the inscription 'DEO SOLI GLORIA'.

HIGHWAYS

The map of Roman Britain shows clearly the genius of the Roman surveyors as road builders. There is a veritable network of highways all over England and Wales: Watling Street from Dover to London, and thence to St Albans, Wroxeter, northwards to Chester and along the North Wales coast; the great Fosse Way from Exeter via Bath to Lincoln, then north to Hadrian's Wall and into the lowlands of Scotland as far as the Wall of Pius between the Forth and the Clyde.

No scientific road building took place at all in Britain for about fourteen centuries after the departure of the Romans, although the first Turnpike Act was passed in 1663. Louis XIV of France (1643–1715) established training centres for road builders, whilst Britain contented herself with mend and botch-up, and the exile in France of our Charles II between 1651 and 1660 may have given him the opportunity of examining French highways and so led to the act of 1663 authorising the erection of tollgates or turnpikes along the main road from London to Edinburgh at which a toll was extracted to defray the cost of road maintenance. The word 'turnpike', now used for motorways in the USA, is a curious survival of a medieval word into the latter half of the twentieth century.

There was then a furious burst of parliamentary activity in connection with highway building, for between 1760 and 1792, over 750 Turnpike Acts were passed. But it was not until pioneer work on new roadmaking techniques had been carried out that British roads began to be really usable. The pioneers were John Smeaton (d 1792), Jack Metcalf (d 1810), Thomas Telford (d 1834) and John Macadam (d 1836) whose name is immortalised wherever roads are built and who, Sir Arthur Quiller-Couch recorded, came to Cornwall in 1798 as a navy victualling officer at Falmouth. Here he practised his experiments in roadmaking, discovering the value of Cornish greenstone for roads, and it is claimed that he built the new turnpike road from Truro Workhouse to Kiggon, now part of A39 between the City and Tresillian. He became general surveyor of all roads in 1827. His grandson William was surveyor to the Truro Turnpike Trust, appointed in 1825 for five years but continuing at least until 1835–6.

The Cornish Turnpike Trusts were established between 1754 and 1863 as follows:

Bodmin 1769, expired in 1866
Callington 1762
Camelford, Wadebridge and St Columb 1760, expired 1869
Creed and St Just-in-Roseland 1761
Hayle Bridge Causeway 1825, expired 1868
Hayle and Redruth 1839, expired 1870
Helston 1760, expired 1864

Launceston 1760, expired 1866
Liskeard 1760, expired 1873
Redruth 1762, expired 1870
St Austell and Lostwithiel 1760, expired 1857
Saltash 1761, expired 1864
Trebarwith Sands Road, 1825
Truro 1754, expired 1870
Penzance to St Just-in-Penwith 1863
All trusts were abolished by 1885.

The population of Cornwall almost doubled between 1801 and 1861 from 192,000 to 369,000 and, with the need for better highways with increasing prosperity, Cornishmen were in the forefront of road building in the generation from 1820 to 1850. The archaeology of these turnpikes can be seen today in the dozens of milestones which the trusts commissioned and in the comparatively few toll cottages left standing at the side of the highway, often characterised by a protruding bay window that was the 'ticket office'. There is an extremely late example of a tollhouse at Tremethick Cross on highway A3071 west of Penzance, built about 1863 at a time when Turnpike Trusts were becoming a thing of the past.

The milestones along Cornish highways are a fascinating study and are a visible link with the trusts and with the contracts they let to masons or to foundries for these appurtenances of the road. Most milestones are of stone but, in the south-east, an occasional mile-iron is to be found of the period when cast-iron was the 'in' metal. Some stones are exceedingly plain and give little away, eg having only an initial letter and a figure, like those found in the Glynn Valley between Bodmin and Liskeard or others between Bodmin and Camelford of which the Cornwall Register (1847) remarks:

The making of the Camelford Turnpike road in 1759 was taken up as a matter of patriotism and to assist the undertaking, the Rev William Phillipps, Rector of Lanteglos cut with his hands the figures on the granite mile-stones which still remain. The like public spirit would be of service in the present day, when mile-stones and direction posts are so much neglected.

Between Truro and Indian Queens are to be found triangular stones bearing a cast-iron plate on each splay, with the distances to London and Falmouth—a reminder of the day when the road was used by long-distance coaches. But on this same road in the vicinity of Mitchell are to be found older milestones beautifully inscribed 'Saint Columb' and with the distance in Roman figures. There is an interesting reference to milestones in Lyson's *Magna Brittania* published in 1814: 'The old road from North Cornwall to Land's End branched off at Mitchell: it has been long disused for carriages though its milestones remain and it keeps its place in the road books.' Some of these old stones are still extant, square on plan with a pyramid at the top and can be seen at intervals along the present A30.

There are to be found all over Cornwall individualistic and curious milestones of local origin. One such is at Crows-an-Wra on the A30 3 miles east of Sennen, cut by Billy Foss. Another is at Gurnards Head on the coast road between St Ives and St Just proclaiming the distance 6 miles to 'ƨTIVƧ'! whilst at Trerule Foot between Torpoint and Liskeard is a stone with the legend '7M·22p·1y to s b', the *very* exact distance to the Saltash steam-bridge. On highway A390 half a mile west of Liskeard is a triangular mile-iron with the information '½ mile to the Cross in Church Street'. Of very different type is an 8ft high granite column on the verge of B3266 near St Tudy; on its summit is a flat square stone, the shallow sides bearing names of towns nearby.

Our final reference to highways is the Torpoint Ferry, that all-important southern link between Devon and Cornwall, over which the first ferry-boat started on 4 July 1791. *Magna Brittania* recorded, 'the Great Road from London to Land's End via Plymouth Dock enters Cornwall at Torpoint' with the footnote that the ferry is impassable in bad weather. Increasing population and prosperity and the growing importance of the naval base, led to ways and means for improving such delays to travellers, so that in '1831' (the actual year was in fact 1834) 'carriages and horses are placed upon the new steam-bridge established by Mr J. M. Rendel, the engineer residing in Plymouth. It is a novel invention for crossing rivers and first applied by Mr Rendel to the Dart and then at Torpoint and Saltash.' The *West Briton* of 5 September 1834 recorded that the new steam-bridge was deemed reliable enough for mail coaches to cross without changing horses!

BRIDGES

Ancient stone bridges across rivers were the first 'industrial' monuments to be protected under the Ancient Monument Acts. Cornwall is rich in bridges, both in stone and in iron, indeed the oldest representation of a Cornish bridge appears on the fourteenth-century seal of the old borough of Grampound, ie *grand-pont*. The late Charles Henderson (1900–33) published his *Old Cornish Bridges* in 1928 recording nearly a hundred, of which there are interesting examples to be seen: Ruthern, west of Bodmin, a Gothic arched structure in blue slate of about mid-fifteenth century; Respryn near Bodmin Road station, carrying the road over the River Fowey on four arches and dating from about 1500; Lerryn, a very simple single arch without parapets of about mid-sixteenth century; Berriow across the River Lynher in Northill parish, repaired, according to the records, in 1640; Nether across the River Tamar on the Holsworthy Road A388; Temple Old Bridge on Bodmin Moor probably built in 1769 when the new 'posting road' was built from Launceston; Wooda that carries the A388 over the River Inny between Launceston and Callington on a 35ft arch bearing a stone inscribed R WISE LANSON 1836.

Henderson's survey was started in 1925 when the inelegant Trevemper Bridge near Newquay was built by the county council. In his preface he wrote, 'we have not even the consolation that the new concrete successors of the old bridges will also be beautiful'. Perhaps these words were heeded, for when the Polson Bridge across the River Tamar (A30) was rebuilt in 1932, the centre arch of granite has such distinction in its design that it might well be mistaken for an early nineteenth-century bridge. The two smaller arches on either side of the main arch are considerably older.

SUBMARINE CABLES

No story of communications in Cornwall is complete without a reference to the submarine telegraph. In July 1866 Brunel's great iron ship the *Great Eastern,* launched in 1859 by means of huge hydraulic presses invented by the Cornish firm Tangye Brothers, successfully completed the laying of the first transatlantic cable from Valentia in south-west Ireland to Newfoundland.

The circumstances that brought the submarine telegraph to Cornwall's shores was the need for a direct cable link with India after the Indian Mutiny 1857–8. Ten years later, in May 1868, the Anglo-Mediterranean Telegraph Company was formed and it laid the cable from Malta to Alexandria—the first section of the India cable. In January 1869, John Pender formed the British Indian Submarine Telegraph Company with the object of laying a cable from Suez to Bombay and, later in the July of that year, he started the Falmouth, Gibraltar & Malta Telegraph Company. Suez to Alexandria was by landline.

The ss *Great Eastern* left Portland, England, in November 1869. She arrived in Bombay the following January and, with other ships, the Suez–Bombay cable was completed by March 1870. A few weeks later, the laying of the Malta–Gibraltar cable started, concurrently with the laying of another link in the Indian chain, that from Gibraltar to Carcavelos in Portugal. The ss *Hibernia,* built in 1860, which had laid part of the Suez–Aden cable, then moved to the Atlantic, took over at Carcavelos and laid the remaining link to Porthcurno, completed on 8 June 1870.

This was the first long-distance chain of direct submarine telegraph in the British Empire; and so was established the first cable station at Porthcurno, known to cablemen for a century as PK. In 1872, all the companies were amalgamated to form the Eastern Telegraph Company, known as Cable & Wireless Ltd since 1934.

Cornwall was linked by cable with Valentia and America when the Western Union cable of America came ashore at Sennen in 1881. The company established its first cable station in a newly built house called 'Amherst', in Hawkins (later Trewithen) Road, Penzance, transferring it to 'Longnor' next door in 1895. Both are still extant. In 1913, it built a new cable station in Alverton, Penzance, which remained in use until October 1965.

The French–American cable also went out from Porthcurno, and its promoters, Compagnie du Télégraphe de Paris à New York, had their offices at 55 Chapel Street, Penzance, in the 1880s. In the 1870s, a need was felt for a direct telephone link between Cornwall and Spain, mainly for the cattle trade; the cable was laid between Bilbao and Cornwall, the Cornish end of it coming ashore at Kennack Sands between the Lizard and Coverack. For about twenty-five years, its owners, the Direct Spanish Telegraph Company, had its office at 25 Church Street in Falmouth, but in the early years of this century they were at Kuggar, a mile inland from Kennack, remaining there until March 1911.

WIRELESS

The story of Poldhu is memorable for, on 12 December 1901, the first wireless signal was transmitted across the Atlantic from the transmitter on Angrouse Cliff to Marconi at Signal Hill, St John's, Newfoundland. Guglielmo Marconi (b Bologna, 1874) had successfully transmitted wireless signals from Lavernock Point near Penarth to Brean Down on the Somerset coast in May 1897. In October 1900 Marconi's Wireless Telegraph Co Ltd began to build a new 25kW wireless station on the cliff top at Poldhu between Mullion and Gunwalloe and it was completed by January 1901. Its designer was John, later Sir Ambrose, Fleming. An elaborate aerial and mast system, an inverted cone of 400 wires supported by a circle of masts

200ft high, was built surrounding the transmitter. A great autumn gale on 17 September destroyed the aerial, and Marconi then replaced it with a simpler one consisting of 60 wires suspended from two 150ft masts. It was from that aerial that Marconi and his assistant Kemp heard 'the faint but distinctive successions of three dots which had crossed the Atlantic from the Cornish cliff top at Poldhu'. The two original 150ft masts were replaced in 1902 by four timber towers and they in turn were replaced with steel tubular masts a decade later. Another wireless station was also built at the Lizard and operated from 1902 to 1918.

Poldhu Radio closed down for public transmissions in June 1922 but it then became a centre for experiments in directional short-wave transmissions, notably by C. S. Franklin who developed at Poldhu the short-wave beam-wireless system in 1923–4 and the coaxial cable, an essential element of our present-day television. In 1920, also at Poldhu, a wireless telephony transmitter was installed which broadcast programmes to the liner SS *Victorian* en route to Canada. It was one of the earliest successful examples of broadcasting and led to the formation of the BBC in 1922.

Poldhu was finally closed down in 1934 and the site cleared by 1937. It is now National Trust property. On the cliff edge today there is a granite memorial erected by the Marconi Company in 1937 and designed by Kelly & Co (Cramb Bros) Ltd of London. On its four faces are bronze plaques recording the history of Poldhu as the pioneer place of telecommunications. Behind the monument in a field, a diligent search reveals the archaeology of those early days of wireless: great concrete anchor blocks for the mast stays; mast bases; the tiled floor of the transmitter building from whence the first signal went out on that winter's day in 1901; and a circular grass-grown rail track about 165ft diameter on which travelled the Franklin beam aerial in the 1920s.

It was as a direct result of this beam-wireless system, that the Empiradio Network was established by Marconi for the Post Office and the Dominion governments—and once more Cornwall played its part. The Canadian beam transmitter was built near Lanivet, opened on 25 October 1926 (Bodmin Radio) to be followed by the South African beam on the same site on 5 July 1927.

And, following from all these pioneering efforts, there was established in July 1962, on a site at Goonhilly only 2½ miles away from Poldhu, the first Post Office satellite communications ground station in Britain, thus once more opening up an entirely new field in telecommunications. Cornwall has witnessed everything from the start of a mail packet service to Falmouth in 1688 to the Telstar Satellite nearly three centuries after.

The Marconi Company in 1953 presented a plaque in memory of their founder which can be seen on a hut situated near the Coastguard look-out at Bass Point, half a mile south-east of Landewednack Church, the Lizard. It reads:

GUGLIELMO MARCONI WHOSE PIONEER WORK IN WIRELESS TELEGRAPHY FOR THE SAFETY OF ALL SEAFARERS WAS FURTHERED IN THIS BUILDING DURING THE FIRST YEARS OF THIS CENTURY.

CHAPTER EIGHT

Quarrying—An Age-old Industry

OVER perhaps twenty centuries of history, the quarrymen of Cornwall have moulded and enhanced the landscape. Castles; two great
churches, St Germans and Truro, eight centuries apart; farmhouses
and farmbuildings; stone walls and hedges; miles of streets lined with
stone-walled buildings and often with stone-slabbed pavements
testify to their industry. The colours and textures vary enormously:
granite in Penzance, St Just and St Ives; yellow-brown soft slate
killas in Truro; harder blue slate in Wadebridge and Camelford and
brown culm in the extreme north. Kilkhampton in the north is
completely different to villages like Mullion or St Buryan in the
south.

One of the early indications of an actual quarry from whence this
building stone came is to be found at St Germans, which was the
cathedral town of Cornwall in Saxon times—bishops of the See of
St Germans are known for about four generations between 930–1050.
The great Norman church here, a priory of the Augustinians, has a
magnificent stone gabled porch on the west façade, having a cross as
its finial, and within it a huge Norman porch of seven orders with
bold zig-zag ornament. It was built about 1160, is unique in Cornwall,
and the masons used the dark elvan stone from Tartan Down Quarry
in the parish of Landrake.

Natural stone is reckoned the most noble of all building materials
and, over the past millennium, millions of tons must have been
quarried in Cornwall for a myriad of purposes, from the walls of
great docks to serpentine ashtrays. In a survey made in 1938, 255
quarries having a face exceeding 20ft in depth were recorded.

SLATE

The historian Norden writing in 1582 claimed 'Menheniot slate is the best in Cornwall' but Dr Borlase in 1758 wrote 'Delabole slate is the finest in the world'. Of interest is the testimony of Richard Carew of Antony writing about 1600:

> In the rest of this earthy description [he has been writing about the Cornish weather, its earth and quality] I will begin with such minerals as her bowels yield forth and then pass on to those things of growing life which upon her face do relieve themselves.
>
> Quarrie stones are of sundrie sorts and serve to divers purposes. For walling, there are rough and slates the rough maketh speedier buildings, the slate surer. For windows, doors and chimnies, Moore-stone carrieth chiefest reckoning. That name is bestowed on it by the Moores or waste ground when the same is found in great quantity, either lying upon the ground or verie little under. This stone with the fairness of his whitish colour, containing certaine glimmering sparkles and countervaileth his great hardness in working with the profit of long endurance.
>
> There are also three other sorts of stones, serving to the same use, and hewed with lesse though differing labour: Pentuan digged out of the sea cliffs and in colour resembleth somewhat gray marble, Caraclouse black, the third taken out of inland quarries. The sea affordeth pebble-stones serving very handsomely for paving of streets and courts.
>
> For covering of houses, there are three sorts of slate. The first and best Blew: the second Sageleaf coloured: the third and meanest Gray. The Blew and so the rest, are commonly found under the walling slate, when the depth hath brought the workmen to the water. This slate is in substance thinne, in colour faire, in waight lighte, in lasting strong, and generally carrieth so good regard as good stone is yeerely conveyed by shipping both to other parts of the realm and also beyond the seas into Britain and Netherland.

Delabole Slate

The story of Delabole, a name that the *Gazetteer of Cornwall* (1884) says was also known as Dinabole, is the story of a slate quarry that has been in production for nearly six centuries. The village, comprising the old settlements of Medrose, Pengelley and Rockhead (Penmaen) is in the large 6,000 acre parish of St Teath whose church

K

is 3 miles away. The *Gazetteer* attributes to Carew the information
that the Delabole Quarry was 300yd × 100yd × 80yd deep but this
does not appear in the first edition of his *Survey* published in 1602.

The Old Delabole Slate Company Limited states that their earliest
mineral lease for slate is dated 1396, in the reign of the last Plan-
tagenet, Richard II. By any standards this is a tremendously long
life for any quarry. It is generally reckoned that the slate was at first
discovered in a stream bed at the junction of two watercourses. To
the east was one ownership, to the west another and, for a long time,
only the latter was worked.

Considerable enlargements were made between 1750 and 1800,
indeed the *Victoria County History* states that in former years 'only
a few men were at work'. This enlargement of the quarry during the
latter half of the eighteenth century is coincident with the impetus of
the Industrial Revolution and the expansion of the metalliferous
mining industry in Cornwall after the introduction of steam power
earlier in the century. This evidence is important since it disposes of
the oft repeated story that 'Delabole quarry has employed 400 men
for 400 years'.

Early in the eighteenth century, the Pengilley quarry had been
worked by various members of the Baker family, of whom Robert
installed waterwheels and horse whims for haulage in 1761. In 1803,
the quarry was up for sale, the *Sherborne Mercury* reporting (11 April
1803) 'the bottoms are kept open by a newly erected water engine';
and Robert Baker's grandson took over. He installed further water-
pumping equipment, whims, and drove a drainage adit southwards
from the quarry floor for ¾ mile.

Nearby another quarry was working, Landwork, that attracted the
attention of Thomas Avery of Boscastle. He purchased a share in it
and soon became the proprietor, forging considerable shipping links
with South Wales ports. In 1833, the main Delabole quarry at
Pengilley was again advertised for lease and, although Avery made a
bid, it was granted to Messrs Grainger & Trickett. This so angered
Avery that he started a 'war', opening rival slate workings at Grove

Quarry to the south-west and Ash Tree to the east. Through his control of Landwork, he diverted the water away from the main Delabole engines, obstructed Grainger & Trickett's access and protracted litigations resulted.

In 1834, a Mr Evans installed the 'Speedwell' steam engine at the main quarry, but later research has indicated that the Camborne engineer, Arthur Woolf, had designed an engine for Delabole about 1810.

By the 1840s, the rivalries at Delabole were coming to an end. The Old Delabole Slate Company was formed and, when Avery's lease at Landwork expired in 1847, he found the opposition too strong and sold all his interests to the new company whose original capital was £15,000, increased to £73,000 by 1859, and a bank loan of £38,000. In 1860, 450 men and 130 boys were employed and 1,200 tons of slate were hoisted daily. Ten thousand tons of roofing slate were produced that year and for years following, transported by 40–50 horse and waggon teams to Port Gaverne and other places of shipment. These teams also hauled huge quantities of slate products to the GWR stations at Launceston and Bodmin Road until the coming of the North Cornwall Railway to Delabole in 1893.

By 1882, the one huge quarry was 1,300ft long and 400ft deep, employing 500 hands. Two large waterwheels, driving Cornish lifts with flat-rods were added for pumping, the water being led to them by hundreds of yards of timber launders or flumes. The fixing of these launders to the faces of the quarry must have been a hazardous operation and there are contemporary photographs of them in the slate company's possession. In times of dry weather, steam power had to be used to work the pumps.

About 1912, the quarry manager was a Welshman named Davies, a lover of bargains. He purchased from the defunct Bethin or Wheal Archer mine in the parish of Advent, a powerful 50ft waterwheel. It was dismantled at the mine, laboriously transported 3 miles to the quarry, taken down into the quarry and there rebuilt. It needed so much water to drive it efficiently that it was never a success. The story is worth recounting of the occasion when, as superintendent of the church Sunday school, Mr Davies was describing to his class the story of the River Jordan. On asking if there were any questions, Tom, a boy who was noted for being blunt, exclaimed 'sir, thee's do want that river for drivin' yur water wheel'. This was too much for the superintendent who had had to suffer much for his 'bargain'. The cane was soon in action!

In 1906, there were seven large steam engines at work in the quarry: 2 for haulage, 3 for driving machinery, 1 for pumping and a new one for haulage up the main 1,000ft incline on a gradient of 1 in 2½. The Ordnance Survey of that year indeed shows three subsidiary inclines as well which, together with five engine houses, the area of the quarry, the spoil tips, the surface buildings and stock yard covered 110 acres.

The big rotative beam-engine at the quarry about 1880 was used for many purposes. Off the main driving shaft there was a bell crank connected to a bob driving a flat-rod to a Cornish lift pump hundreds of feet away. Another crank drove a large haulage drum from no 1 incline a quarter of a mile away. Another haulage cable ran over the roof of the engine house up to the head of yet another incline. If this wasn't enough, there was also a water-frame saw, also driven by this one engine, destroyed in 1914 at the scrap yard in Hayle, the birthplace and the graveyard of so much of Cornwall's industrial greatness.

The Delabole Quarry has seen all types of power. From waterwheels to Pelton turbines, steam engines to gas engines, then diesel engines and finally to electricity. All the historic machines went to the scrap yards in the 1920s and the power for haulage on the one 1,100ft incline today is provided by large Mather & Platt/Igranic electric engines made in Manchester and Bedford and installed in 1929.

The editor of the *Handbook for Travellers in Devon and Cornwall* (1850), Thomas Clifton Paris (son of Dr John Paris, founder of the Royal Geological Society of Cornwall in 1814) was deeply interested in industrial techniques. He described the quarry thus:

Two villages owe their origin to the Delabole quarries, Pengelly and Medrose. These quarries present one of the most astonishing and animated scenes imaginable. The traveller suddenly beholds 3 enormous pits, excavated by the uninterrupted labour of centuries, slowly encroaching upon the domain of the farmer. Throngs of men engaged in various noisy employments, steam engines are lifting with a harsh sound their ponderous arms [obviously the 'bobs'] and raising loaded trucks from pit depths. Masses of stone slowly ascending guide-chains to stages overhanging the pits.

The most interesting quarry is 260 ft deep but the upper pit is the largest though now nearly exhausted. Upon the edge of each quarry is the Papote Head or platform from which guide chains are stretched like the shrouds of a ship to pit bottom. The slate, after blasting, is placed on a truck, which being attached to a wheel traversing a guide chain, is drawn up to the Papote head by steam engine. Moveable hatches are run out 14 ft over the face on to which the truck lands and is then drawn away by horses to the workshops.

The water is pumped from the quarry by water-wheel, and the slate is taken by wagons drawn by two bullocks and a horse, to the beach at Port Gavorne to be loaded into ships. Boscastle is also used in the winter since it affords better shelter.

The 'Papote' heads—the name seems to be synonymous with 'parapet' and was usually 'puppet' to the men—were dangerous and led, as the *Handbook* records, to 'melancholy accidents' so that incline haulage replaced them. They are shown on plate, p 143 and were probably installed by Thomas Avery.

The company employed women and girls at the quarry until 1855, and although their labour was then dispensed with, in all fairness it was stated that they were of equal ability to the men. They were the equivalent of the 'balmaids' employed in the mines and clay works until 1913. By 1871 the labour force was 580 but the following year it had dropped to 466, probably in consequence of the mining depression and the emigration of so many Cornishmen abroad and it remained at about this figure for many years. It was given as 400 in 1935.

The North Cornwall Railway which came to Delabole in October 1893 was at once connected to the quarry slate-wharf, indeed the directors were so happy to see it arrive that they gave the railway company the land for constructing the line around western rim of the quarry to Delabole station. They also purchased several narrow-gauge locomotives for their own network of tramways, two were named *E. Jago* and *Sir John T. Firbank.* The new railway system caused the demise of Port Gaverne, Port Isaac and Boscastle as slate ports.

In 1873, the quarry produced 242,000 tons of slate products; in 1880 (the peak) 360,000 tons, an average of 1,000 a day; in 1893 it produced 147,000 tons and in 1903 the figure was 274,000. At this time, quarrymen's wages were 21s (£1.05) a week and those of the lower grade of workmen 17s (85p). To make a day's wage, the quarryman had to move 50 tons of slate. Mr C. E. Leese, late of Camelford, recorded in 1937 that the quarry was 470ft in depth, employed 350 and produced 10,000 tons of slate a year, together with 250,000 tons for the waste tip.

Delabole slate has been used for many things. Over the centuries it has produced slates to cover hundreds of square miles of roofs. The most attractive is the scantle roof, using slates of different sizes and needing 700 to cover a 'square' 10ft × 10ft. Their use was mainly confined, sixty years ago, to West Cornwall and Belgium. Another form of roofing is large ragslates requiring 130 per square, used much in North and East Cornwall in the nineteenth century for farm buildings. The other products of this remarkable industry were slate slabbing for kitchen floors—a cold and merciless scrubbing job for Victorian housemaids; window-sills; corn chests; vats; mantelpieces and water cisterns up to 2,000 gallons capacity.

Today the quarry still continues in production though with a labour force of only sixty men. The surface is 700ft above sea level and the quarry floor 200ft; ie it is 500ft deep. It is 1¼ miles around the circumference. As the roofing slate is now a hand-made product, it is inevitably costly; it would be sad to think that the time may come when no more is produced. Other products are enormous quantities of slate powder (Delafila) for the plastic, cosmetics and paint industries; slate granules for surfacing *concrete* roofing tiles; and 6in × 4in and 4in × 4in, ¼in thick tiles. Also available is building and hedging stone. The name 'Delabole Slate' is now protected by law.

Carew wrote of this slate being exported to Netherland over 350 years ago. After British Railways abandoned practically all the former LSWR lines in 1967 and the rail link to the quarry was cut, it was fascinating to discover at Wadebridge station in the autumn of 1968 a train of slate-powder wagons. They were made in San Sebastian by Herederos de Ramon Mujica and leased to Sinotra et Cie of Paris. One conjectured they contained Cornish powdered slate destined for the French cosmetics industry or for a plastics factory in Germany.

Other Slate Quarries

The basic rock over a large part of the district round Delabole has been responsible for quarries other than Delabole itself. Lanterden (or Tom Sweet's) Quarry was at Hole Beach, Trebarwith, believed to have been opened about 1700 and last worked in a small way in 1930. This undertaking shipped its products from Port William.

At Tintagel, the Cliff Quarries, known as Lambshouse Quarry and Long Grass Quarry, were last worked in the 1930s. They were opened about 1800 and in 1905 had been working continuously for half a century, employing at that time 42 men and using steam haulage. The waste was thrown into the sea and the slates were shipped from Tintagel. The remains of this industry are visible on the cliffs.

South-east of Tintagel, at Trewarmett in the Trebarwith Valley, are three quarries now disused: Bowithick opened about 1823 and still operating in 1912; Prince of Wales which started in 1871 and continued at least to the 1890s, and where the old engine house still stands; and the Jefferies Pit last worked in 1928. East of Bossiney, near Tintagel, the Trevillet Quarry closed about 1958, and Kelly's *Directory* (1935) indicates 'Old Bowithick Slate Quarries, Trevillet' which is 2 miles north-east of Trewarmett.

Apart from the Old Delabole Slate Quarry, there are now only four small quarries in operation producing paving, building stone and 'rustic tiles'; they are Trecarne, Jenkins, Penpethy and King's Down. Penpethy Delabole Quarries Ltd appears in the 1935 *Directory*.

Of interest to the railway historian is the old Westwood Quarry opened about 1853 by the Cornwall Railway at the east end of the Glynn Valley not far from Doublebois station near Liskeard. The stone is hard brown slate-killas, selected by Brunel for the building of the piers for twenty railway viaducts between Saltash and Coombe-by-St Stephens, west of St Austell. The tall slender piers of the St Pinnock Viaduct in the Glynn Valley rising 140ft above the valley floor and built 1854–5, are a testimonial to the judgement of their designer and have been carrying trains now for 113 years. With the exception of Coombe-by-Saltash Viaduct which was rebuilt of Devon grey limestone in 1893, most Cornish railway viaducts are built of local granite from various quarries. Notable examples are Moorswater (1881), St Austell (1898) and Angarrack (1886).

GRANITE

The diverse nature of Cornwall's geology has given rise to quarries producing several different types of stone over the centuries. It may well have been the use of granite from St Breward parish in the late 1750s for the building of the fourth Eddystone lighthouse (p 149) that gave wider publicity to the excellence of this stone. It is so hard and durable that few think of Cornwall without thinking of granite and indeed the description 'Cornwall's granite cliffs' is applied indiscriminately along her coastline. There is in fact only a very small mileage indeed of granite along the coast, about 25 miles out of 312.

In the *Gazetteer of Cornwall* (1884) the principal granite-quarrying areas of Cornwall are shown as Mabe, Stithians, Constantine and Wendron lying between Penryn and Helston; Linkinhorne and St Breward on the east and west sides respectively of the Bodmin Moor granite mass; and the quarries in the far west St Just area. *The Handbook for Travellers* states: 'Penryn granite has long been known for its fine grain and is the material of which the Waterloo Bridge was constructed. This was between 1811 and 1817 by the engineer John Rennie (1761–1821). Mabe granite was quarried for this bridge, shipped from Penryn Quay to the Surrey shore of the Thames, worked in the fields nearby, and then moved to the bridge site on a horse tramway. The great naval docks at Chatham, dating from the early part of the nineteenth century, are also part of the 'industrial archaeology' of the quarrymen of Mabe and, in this century, the stone of Carnsew Quarry in the same district was taken out to the Fastnet reef off the south-western coast of Ireland for building the present lighthouse there. In the heyday of the industry during the first half of the nineteenth century, 20,000 tons of granite were shipped each year through the port of Penryn, worth at the quarry 1s 9d (9p) per cubic foot in the 1850s. The price today averages £1.85.

The *Handbook for Travellers* remarked in 1865: 'Lamorna formerly one of the most romantic spots on the coast of West Penwith is now, being selected for the site of some granite works, little better than a masons yard.' A quarry was opened on the south side of the cove but the quality was poor and the main source of stone was from the north side. During its life of about sixty years 1850–1910, huge quantities of stone were raised and sent to London for the construction of the Thames Embankment. A Blondin was erected (described on p 122) to transfer the stone across the cove to the new pier. It was then loaded into barges and taken out to waiting ships. The dangerous coast caused this method of transportation to be abandoned and was followed by the installation of a steam engine to hoist stone to the cliff summit then to be taken by road into Penzance and Newlyn. There is a fine painting by the late Stanhope Forbes at Treneere Manor, Penzance, called 'The Quarry Team', portraying vividly the haulage of Lamorna granite by horses. The quarry was last used about half a century ago to raise stone for the reconstruction of the Penzance–Mousehole coast road.

In several places in Cornwall, porphyry or porphyritic granite was worked in the past. At Gunnislake on the Tamar, the notable Pearson's Quarry (1808–1905) produced a fine pink stone. The *Handbook for Travellers* records that 'boulders of porphyry were lying about the moors of Luxulyan and it was from one of them, of a deep pink colour blotched with black hornblende, that the sarcophagus of the Duke of Wellington was made in 1853–5. This block, found on the land of William Rashleigh of Menabilly, weighed 70 tons: was wrot by steam power and over two years made into the sarcophagus at a cost of £1100'. Two quarries producing this stone were working as late as the 1930s: Tregarden at Luxulyan and Colkerrow in Lanlivery. Tregarden still produces crushed stone.

Methods of Drilling

In the heyday of the Cornish granite industry, when huge quantities of magnificent stone were quarried for monumental buildings like Norman Shaw's New Scotland Yard, or the Gateshead Bridge in Newcastle-on-Tyne, the whole operation was centred on the production of the largest blocks without crack or blemish. Cornish granite is generally found with cracks in the rock, ie joints, and blasting was undertaken to open up the joint and loosen the block from its bed, black powder being used for the purpose. Two holes were drilled in the block, powder was tamped into them with a wooden rod, and then fired by either electricity or safety fuse. Before the days of compressed-air drills, this initial drilling had to be carried out by hand. Three or four men were employed, one holding a rod and two delivering blows from heavy sledge hammers. These steel rods were up to 18ft long and 4in diameter and had to be held and twisted by two quarrymen after each double blow from the hammers.

After a large block was loosened it had to be cut into smaller pieces for lifting. This was done by drilling a line of small holes about 3in depth, putting two steel 'feathers' into each one, and then driving a steel-wedge plug between them. Then starting at one end of the line, the quarrymen would tap each plug once, repeating the process three or four times until the rock was split by the gradual tightening of the wedges.

The Decline of the Industry

Fifty years ago, the Cornish granite industry was still extremely active with about thirty-five working quarries. The names Freeman and McLeod were known all over Britain and further afield. George McLeod at one time was at the De Lank Quarry (pp 172–3) and then about 1936, G. McLeod Ltd of Mabe merged with John Freeman Sons & Co Ltd of Penryn to form J. Freeman & McLeod of Penryn. It owned and operated as many as 60 quarries giving employment to 1,500 men, producing granite from quarries with evocative Cornish names like Polkanuggo, Rosemanewas and Pelastine in the Mabe district, and the Cheesewring Quarry at Linkinhorne, where the stone sleeper-blocks of the old tramway are still to be seen.

In 1947, the Cornish & Devon Granite Masters' Association produced a *Handbook*. In the foreword, Sir Edward Bolitho of Trengwainton wrote, 'Cornwall has always been proud of her Granite. It is a hard stone and a hard taskmaster too. The quarrying and cutting is a great art and one which should never be allowed to die. In the interests of Cornwall I hope that Granite will once again be used in the construction of buildings.' At that time, there were 43 members of the association; 37 of them based in Cornwall. About 10 members remain today, with working quarries at Lestraynes, Rame Cross, Mabe; the De Lank Quarry at St Breward; and Spargo's Quarry at Trolvis, Longdowns, Penryn. It should, however, be recorded that the international firm of Limmer & Trinidad Asphalt are now working the old granite quarry of Hantergantick that adjoins De Lank.

The quarrying of granite and its general use for facing buildings began to decline sharply after 1920, one of the last large buildings to be faced wholly with granite is the Truro County School for Girls in Treyew Road completed in 1927. Three smaller buildings, all admirable examples of fine stonework, are Barclays Bank premises in

Coinage Hall Street, Helston, and Chapel Street, Camborne, both
about 1930; and those in Killigrew Street, Falmouth, built as late as
1956.

The quarry at Trolvis is of interest since it is one of the few
remaining family businesses producing, in the main, stone for the
monumental mason. The face is about 100ft depth and the stone is
raised, after blasting, by a traditional old Cornish quarry-crane but
now operated by compressed air. Further west near Paul are two
quarries producing granite for the monumental mason. They are
Castallack worked by Obed Prowse and Carn Lankin worked by
Jesse Prowse, and have been worked since 1840.

De Lank Quarry

De Lank, the name has been known to stonemasons for over 200
years and the quarry is still producing perhaps the best Cornish
granite now available. Cornish De Lank Granite Quarries Company,
owned by the Sheffield steel firm of Thomas W. Ward, are justly
proud of their first internationally known product, the fourth Eddystone lighthouse completed in 1759 to the design of John Smeaton.
The stone for this great rock tower was hewn in a quarry at De Lank,
still called 'The Eddystone' though no longer used, hauled to Bradford's Quay at Wadebridge, there fashioned together and shipped out
to the Eddystone reef, a distance of about 160 miles. Other fine
examples of the archaeology of these quarrymen of St Breward are
the Beachy Head lighthouse off the Sussex coast 1901 and the present
Eddystone completed in 1882. Huge quantities of De Lank granite
were exported for constructing the great docks at Singapore and
Gibraltar in the 1930s and also for the Thames bridges at Putney
(1884), Lambeth (1932) and Chelsea (1934). Another Thames bridge,
one that is perhaps as much evocative of the London scene as any
structure, is the famous Tower Bridge, opened in 1894 and on whose
design worked Marc, Isambard Kingdom Brunel's son. Its great
towers are built of De Lank granite. An unusual commission for the

quarry in recent years was for large blocks of stone for a Yugoslavian steel works to be used as 'skid' blocks.

In 1929, the De Lank Quarry had a labour force of 150: today it is 56, reflecting the fact that the total number of quarrymen in Cornwall is but a small fraction of those employed at the turn of the century. The cost of quarrying and the wastage of material—at most only about 10 per cent of the stone removed is eventually used—both take their toll; but commissions still come and in the winter of 1968–9 De Lank was producing large 2in thick slabs of stone for facing a new chain-store in Torquay.

To cope with the ever-increasing costs of production, a new method of obtaining the stone from the quarry has been evolved, the 'thermic lance', used only for igneous rock. A mixture of oxygen and paraffin is blown into a water-cooled combustion chamber and there ignited at 3,500°F. The hot gas passes out through a jet nozzle at a speed of 500ft per sec and this high-velocity flame is directed against the face of the stone. The contact area expands and flakes off and, dependent on the hardness of the stone, the lance can cut through 12–20ft per hour. The old water-turbines in the valley below the quarry that used to drive a frame-saw cutting granite blocks at a rate of 4–5in per *day*, have now been superseded by Norwegian (Bergsli) wire saws using a continuously moving high-tensile twisted steel wire cutting through granite at 9in per *hour*. The turbines now operate machines to produce compressed air for the cranes and drills used in the quarry.

POLYPHANT AND SERPENTINE

Two stones used for decorative purposes deserve a mention. At Polyphant in the parish of Lewannick, 5 miles south-west of Launceston, are ancient quarries producing polyphant stone (the geologist calls this stone serpentinised picrite) which was used for the building of Launceston Castle. The quarries were reopened in the 1860s and extensively worked, latterly for fine memorial tablets of which there are examples in Truro Cathedral.

On the Lizard peninsula are found small quarries producing serpentine. The builders of the medieval churches at Grade, Landewednack and Ruan Minor used this stone and it was claimed in the
Illustrated London News of 2 September 1854 that 'the Arrises are
still sharp even after centuries'. The earliest mention of the commercial serpentine-working at the Lizard is in the 1820s and in his
Parochial History of Cornwall Davies Gilbert states that the serpentine factory existed in 1838, about the time that the famous geologist
Sir Thomas de la Beche suggested Signal Staff Hill as a good source
for the stone.

In 1848, John Organ, John Bromley and Richard Millet formed
the Penzance Serpentine Company employing thirty-seven workers
in their factory at Wherrytown. This followed the visit to Penzance
of Queen Victoria in 1846 when she admired serpentine so much that
she ordered a table and other pieces for her new house, Osborne, then
being built in the Isle of Wight. A Mr Murphy who was associated
with this industry brought to Cornwall 'Blue John' turners from
Derbyshire. The Penzance company obtained its stone from Hawker's
Sett and there were other quarries, such as Devil's Frying Pan opened
in 1825, Long Alley and Holestrow.

The royal patronage helped the industry and £2,000 of manufactured serpentine was sent to the Great Exhibition of 1851, where,
according to *The Illustrated Exhibitor: 1851*, 'a prize medal was
awarded to J. ORGAN for font, obelisks etc of serpentine marble from
the Lizard, Cornwall'.

About 1853 the Lizard Serpentine Company was formed by a Mr
Henry Cox and, at the ruins of Poltesco factory, can still be seen a
lintel inscribed 'L.S.C. 1866'. Kelly's *Directory* of 1873 records that
the serpentine factory at Poltesco, producing marble for interior
decorations, was operated by the Poltesco Marble Company (W. B.
Simons, manager) and later, in 1887, it employed eighty hands. There
is an extant photograph showing that it was powered by a 25ft
waterwheel. By 1893 the setts were surrendered and there is no
mention of the factory in Kelly's *Directory* of 1897. In the 1930s it

was recorded that 'the Lizard's serpentine is a beautiful marble of a dark green colour variated with veins of purple, red, white, and scarlet and is manufactured into ornaments, the industry contributing to the support of the village'. The trade still continues, small articles such as ashtrays, table-lamps, and models of lighthouses being made, and popular with tourists.

CRUSHED STONE

The industrial archaeology of the Cornish quarrying industry must include a brief reference to the production of crushed stone for road and railway metal and as the basic ingredient for concrete manufacture. The *Gazetteer of Cornwall* (1884) refers to 'Greenstone, which is much used for macadam [after John Macadam] all over the country and hornblende schist is extensively quarried at Porthalla near the mouth of the Helford River for re-metalling the highways. Elvan is also quarried for the same purpose.'

At Porthoustock, south of Porthalla (now Porthallow) the first of two quarries was opened about 1895 on the north side of the cove by the St Keverne Stone Company: the later one was opened in 1906 and is still being worked by the West of England Road Metal Company. Yet another quarry of long standing is in operation at Hone Quarry at Dean Point, St Keverne, reopened about 1946. Both have piers for shipment of stone.

At Penlee, Newlyn, there is a very large greenstone (blue elvan) quarry, originally opened about 1890. It not only produces crushed elvan but also granite from the Castle-an-Dinas Quarry in the parish of Ludgvan. When it was originally opened, the stone was used as ships' ballast to be sold at the next port. In this way Penlee stone became well known for road metalling and is now exported to European ports. This quarry is noteworthy for its railway, the most southerly in Britain, that conveys the stone from the crushers along the shore to the South Pier where it is discharged into ships' holds. Preserved at the quarry is an engine, built by the German firm of

Arthur Koppel of Berlin in 1900 and named *Penlee* in 1914 'to disguise its German origin'. It served the quarry for over half a century.

There are about 17 quarries in Cornwall today producing crushed stone; probably about 200 more have been abandoned, their archaeology lying under water or buried by dense undergrowth where nature has clothed the scars. It is perhaps of some consolation to record that some of them, like Cheesewring, still have their value as geological monuments or have become nature reserves.

CHAPTER NINE

Other Industries

FOOD PROCESSING
Watermills

T H E harnessing of flowing water to provide power to turn wheels and thus machinery for food production is at least 2,000 years old and is an integral part of Cornwall's industrial history.

In the Morrab Gardens, Penzance, there can be seen two granite mortars discovered at Trewavas Head, Breage, in 1867 and considered to be of the later Stone Age. Dr William Borlase of Ludgvan commented in his *Observations on the Isles of Scilly* (1756):

> There is but one corn mill in Scilly, worked by wind at Penynys. If there is no wind so that the windmill cannot work or if the mill is broke, every house is furnished with a handmill for grinding corn between two stones, the upper one turned by means of a stick, 1½ ins in diameter and 5ft long, the upper end fixed into a hole in a beam overhead.

This was the quern of which Blackie's *Dictionary* says 'from the Saxon *crywn* a hand mill for grinding corn used at one time by Highlanders in Scotland'. It was the first attempt to save the drudgery of the pestle and mortar.

But, because of the uncertainties of wind power and the everlasting drudgery of hand milling—it has been estimated that a woman, whose job it was, pounding the mortar from dawn to dusk, could produce enough flour to feed eight, and the wear on the lass was no doubt considerable!—the water-powered mill evolved.

In 'Water Driven Prime Movers' in *Engineering Heritage*, Paul Wilson, the historian of water-power, wrote:

> If, in the year 1900, such a thing as an United Nations survey of the utilisation of water power throughout the world could have been undertaken, it might well have found that the ancient *Nora* wheels, originally evolved

L   177

twenty centuries ago, still being used in many Mediterranean countries, and Norse mills would have been found in the Scottish islands and Ireland.

This type of mill spread from the Mediterranean into Portugal and northwards to Ireland, the Isle of Man, Wales, Scotland and Norway where it multiplied to such an extent that it became generally known as the Norse mill. Cornwall lies in this path of travel and a millstone found at Trewoofe near Lamorna is almost certain to be from such a mill. It is roughly rectangular with a circular depression 27in diameter, sunk by wear between $\frac{1}{2}$ and 1in, with a central hole 4in across. Through this hole the axle or shaft was driven and below the horizontally placed stone the blades of the wheel sometimes vertical, sometimes at an angle, were fixed to the axle. The water was projected on to the blades by means of a launder and thus the axle and the stone turned, resting on a fixed nether stone. From such a crude machine, there gradually evolved over the centuries the large water-powered mills that have continued to this day.

In the study of this subject, 9 October 932 AD is important for, on that day, King Athelstan's charter to the Oratory at St Buryan signed by himself (there is a copy made in 1238 in the diocesan archives at Exeter) contains a definite reference to the Melynon, the mill of the ash tree, at Treen—a corn mill that worked right through to this century.

The *Domesday Survey* records the sites of five watermills in Cornwall at Gwithian; Cargoll in St Newlyn East; Trevisquite, St Mabyn; Liskeard and Dunheved or Launceston. Five hundred years later, Richard Carew's *Survey of Cornwall* mentions mills briefly in two places. 'In the Westerne most parts of Cornwall they carrie their Barley to the mill within 8 to 9 weekes from the time of sowing' and, in a reference to Saltmills 'the inhabitants made use of divers creekes of the sea for gristmills, the weight of the ebb drying an under-shoote wheel.'

Cornelius Vermuyden, born in the little Dutch town of St Maartensdijk in Zeeland in 1590, came to England in 1621 to advise on the draining of a large area of fen in North Lincolnshire. He was knighted in 1629 and, as an old man in 1672, he made the long trip to Falmouth to advise on the construction of a lengthy channel to bring water from Trescobeas to power a corn mill in Swanpool Street.

John Smeaton FRS (1724–92), who was in Cornwall in the mid-1750s seeking granite for his Eddystone lighthouse and again about 1767 for the building of St Ives harbour, did much work to produce more efficiency from the waterwheel. The force of a full flow of water pouring on to a wheel caused lack of efficiency since air was trapped at the back of the bucket or float. Smeaton diagnosed this and introduced a narrow slit to enable the air to escape so that the full weight of water was applied to make the wheel revolve. The next improvement was to allow the full escape of the tail race so that the speed was unimpeded. His wheels, originally made of timber, were brought to the full pitch of development and then he introduced cast iron for axles and later all-metal wheels, although wheels of both materials continued to be made until very recent times. The late Arthur Saundry of Penzance, to whom much is owed for recording many water-powered mills in West Cornwall, has written, 'every wheel and every mill was an individual'.

The constant industry for centuries in Cornwall has been agriculture, and fast-flowing streams and rivers, rising high in the high hills, have been in continual use over many generations to provide water-power. Although the *Handbook for Travellers in Devon and Cornwall* (1865) records so much fascinating detail about metal mining, china-clay working and the new railways, it says nothing at all about that quiet industry that had been part and parcel of the rural scene for generations, the production of flour and other products. One must surmise that the village mill was so commonplace that no one thought twice about it. It was a normal part of the community.

How much the village relied on its mill. The farmer grew the crop and harvested it by hand-scything until the machine age, sold it to the miller and he in turn relied on a good supply of water at the right time, and upon the ingenuity of the foundries and their millwrights to keep the mill going. The production of huge metal gear wheels, their teeth made of applewood or hornbeam, was skilled engineering work and must have given rise to employment for hundreds of men and helped to keep in production many of the forty or more Cornish foundries having their origins at the end of the eighteenth century. There was also a great deal of skilled timbering needed for all the processes of making flour, and if one thinks of the time before railways, and contrasts it with huge roller mills that now despatch tons of flour six days a week in huge tank-waggons on our roads all over the country, it can be appreciated how the efficiency of the village mill was of extreme importance to the life of a largely rural-based people. It is perhaps significant that a special prayer was composed for the first *Prayer Book* (1549) containing this petition: 'Send us, we beseech thee, in this our necessity, such moderate rain and showers, that we may receive the fruits of the earth.' Note 'moderate' rain: immoderate would have turned the wheel of the mill so fast that heaven knows what would have happened! Grain for the farmer was grist for the miller.

In the 1873 edition of Kelly's *Directory of Cornwall* there were 313 millers listed. Ten years later, the *Directory* indicated a little under 300, the majority of whom were shown as operators of watermills. By 1935, the number had dropped to exactly 100, of which 97 were powered only by water. World War I had been an Indian summer for the rural mills, but when the new Soviet government, in a bid for world trade in 1922, sold grain at far below world prices, there was a great slump. Arthur Saundry of Penzance claimed that the last completely new watermill to be built in Cornwall was at Trelowarren south-east of Helston in 1922. It was a flour mill equipped with the latest machinery.

Some of the names of these millers of the 1930s are almost reminiscent of Dylan Thomas! Mrs Alberta Higman, Pillaton Mill, St Mellion; Goldsworthy Penwarden of Charlestown; Jethro Burden, Treglum Mill, Tresmeer; not to mention Fred Bunkum of Berrio Mill, South Hill. In 1873 there was Ezekiah Spare of St Breward,

miller and shoemaker! In dozens of remote valleys from Coombe
Mill in the furthest north in Morwenstow parish, west of Kilkhamp-
ton, worked by the Tape Brothers and now Landmark Trust property, its machinery in situ, to Crean Mill 3 miles east of Land's End,
mill streams splashed over waterwheels to set stones in motion. On
the Lizard peninsula Harry Tripcony's mill was at Tregidden in
St Keverne: further up the south coast, Tubb's watermill at St
Michael Caerhayes was operated by Mrs Yelland; there was Sam
Willing's mill at Boga in Lanreath, and the Glamorgan Mills at
St Dominick in the Tamar Valley. Two flour mill names are interesting as being significant of an earlier industry: Callestick, St Agnes,
where water-power was once used for smelting through an air-blast;
and Tucking Mill at Warbstow worked by George Petherick, the
survival of a fulling mill that in all probability turned over to flour
production after the fulling trade had gone to Yorkshire and the
Cotswolds generations ago.

During the past thirty-five years, economic pressures have forced
practically all these small mills to close down, and the price of scrap
metal has meant that most of the historic machinery has gone. The
scrap-metal drive during World War II was responsible for further
losses. Now, the watermills have nearly all gone for ever throughout
Cornwall. The last working flour mill in the south-west of the county,
at Roskennals, Newbridge, in Sancreed parish, closed at Michaelmas
1970. A 13ft wheel drove a pair of 50in stones. In mid-Cornwall, at
Lavethan in the Camel valley below Blisland, and close by the
picturesque Wenford Bridge railway, is Lavethan Mill, operated by
W. Keat & Son, where a 15ft diameter wheel made at Wadebridge in
1921 still drives very old mill machinery. The mill itself is of the
seventeenth century and Mr T. Keat was here a century ago. At
Egloshayle near Wadebridge, an unusual 20ft diameter undershot
paddle wheel still drives the mill at Hingham (plate, p 144). Alsia
Mill in St Buryan parish closed in 1966 but its timber wheel and
machinery are intact.

A fine watermill recently stripped of its wheel and machinery was

Penboa lying in a valley between Helston and Gweek, and there was another in a remote part of St Wenn parish at Trewithen, operated by Jonathan Buse in the thirties. This was a product of the Oatey & Martin Foundry at Wadebridge and the date 1798 is on a beam inside the mill. At Bossava Mill in Lamorna, a 1907 wheel of Isaac Willey's Foundry in Helston still exists; at Carthew, Newbridge, the machinery is intact although disused since 1943, the iron wheel a product of Holman's Foundry, St Just; while at Carthew near St Austell is another fine mill with its old wheel, the building bearing a plaque having a representation of a millstone, the date '1837' and the initials 'IL'.

It was to try and rescue what little there is left that a new society was formed in Truro in January 1969, the Cornish Waterwheel Preservation Society now merged, as the Trevithick Society, with the older Cornish Engines Preservation Society founded in October 1935. The society says, 'Cornwall is in process of losing the last of its water wheels, a feature of the county for centuries. The Society aims to save some of the few remaining examples before the opportunity is lost for ever.' Apart from its concern to save surviving water-powered machinery connected with mining, the society is interested in Gweek flour mill with its two wheels, and the last tide mill in Cornwall at Antony Passage near Saltash of the 1860s and long disused.

There is now a world-wide interest in the archaeology of industry and industrial processes. In 1895, in a book of photographs published by the Werner Publishing Company in Chicago, there is shown a watermill in a valley that might well have been taken in Cornwall. The caption reads:

> Within a few miles of Philadelphia stands Germantown. Here some of the earliest colonists settled and Roberts' Mill survives. Old mills in America are so rare that any old bit like this mill attracts attention. One could hardly follow the bank of any little stream in England for more than a mile or two without finding an old mill such as this, but before the American country had been opened up, the old regime of small local industries and the use of water power had yielded to the more energetic role of steam power. The day

may yet come when seekers after the picturesque in America will have to be propitiated by having water-mills preserved.

A prophetic utterance of three-quarters of a century ago in the United States since the US Government National Parks Service is now restoring such places.

Horse Mills

In the *Journal of Industrial Archaeology* (Feb 1968) Professor Frank Atkinson wrote about farm machinery powered by horses, or even by cattle, which were quite common as draught animals in the mid-nineteenth century. These horse mills were located in a wheel house built on as a single storey addition to a barn, often square or hexagonal and about 25ft across. A large inverted crown gear would be turned by a horizontal beam to which two horses would be harnessed; as they walked in a circle, the crown gear would drive a pinion thus turning the shaft. Generally the drive-shaft would run through the wall to drive a thrashing machine inside the barn. Some examples of these mills in Cornwall are:

1 At Trelights near Port Isaac in North Cornwall which came to light in 1967 in the course of alterations to the building. Only a part of the machinery remains.
2 At Restronguet House Farm near Mylor Bridge where there exists a large iron-roofed open barn in which the horses or cattle turned the great gear. Arthur Saundry recorded that three horses pulled continuously, with a fourth used rather like a governor, pulling or backing to regulate the speed. The horizontal wheel actuated a large vertical gear in the adjoining barn.
3 Nearby there is a similar mill at Enys Farm, whilst a third was at Roskrow Farm north-west of Penryn close by the junction of highways A393 and A394.
4 An old horse mill from Canaglaze, Altarnon, that used to drive farm machinery, has been salvaged by the Trevithick Society

which will re-erect it on another site where it will be put in
working order.

5   Another horse mill has recently come to light at Lower Town
Farm on St Agnes in the Scillies.

Wind-power

Cornish historians are in the debt of Mr H. L. Douch, Curator of
the Royal Institution of Cornwall, for his book (1963) on the subject
of Cornish windmills. He says, so rightly:

> The subject of wind power has been surprisingly ignored by Cornish
> historians. The musical sound of falling water and the hiss of steam have
> deafened Cornish ears to the one sound of which they should need no
> reminding, the soughing of the wind. The windmill has been at best con-
> sidered a strange contraption occasionally built by some Cornish eccentric!

Yet the Cornish windmill spans six and a half centuries from 1225 to
1875. In East Anglia, the windmill was generally a tapered brick
tower like the National Trust mill at Burnham Overy in Norfolk.
Others like the one at Madingly on the outskirts of Cambridge are
built entirely of timber and closely resemble those in the Netherlands.
The Cornish mill, however, was a 30ft high circular stone tower
about 11–12ft diameter, and far closer in design to mills found to
this day in Spain and Portugal.

Mr Douch's survey has revealed about seventy windmill sites, used
for grinding corn, scattered along the south coast from Maker to
Marazion—a naval chart of 1820 reveals one between Marazion and
Long Rock; there were two sites at St Ives and then others along the
north coast between St Columb and Morwenstow. Inland sites were
recorded at places like St Erme, Lanlivery, Michaelstow, Week St
Mary and St Ive.

Six 'Martello-like' towers survive as the archaeology of wind-
power. They are:

1   At Maker, on the south bank of the Millbrook Estuary near
    Cremyll, a 25ft high tower of local stone with very thick walls

and 12ft internal diameter. It could be late Elizabethan.

2   At Fowey, in the grounds of Fowey Hall, at one time the residence of Sir Charles Hanson. This is a 20ft mill tower, converted into a 'folly' about the turn of the century by the insertion of a mock-Norman door and slit windows.

3   At Landewednack on the Lizard, the most southerly parish in Britain. Here the tower of an old windmill just survives, 30ft high, its walls built of local serpentine: but its slated conical roof has gone.

4   On the road leading westward from Padstow, in the hamlet of Windmill, the stone base of one of two windmills left in North Cornwall has survived. Its stone walls are battered, and on the north face is a narrow slit window with pointed arch. On its summit, there is now a concrete water tank.

5   The other mill tower is on the east side of the Camel Estuary on the 250ft summit of Carlyon Hill in St Minver parish, and it is still a prominent landmark. It is 30ft high with thick slate walls, built dry, and was originally rendered and limewashed.

6   On the top of Buzza Hill on St Mary's in Scilly a circular stone tower survives of the New Mill, a windmill built in 1820 that continued working until late in the century (plate, p 126). It is understandable that this building was known as the 'Spanish mill' as it so closely resembles similar buildings that existed there and elsewhere in the Mediterranean. It was rebuilt in 1902 to commemorate the visit of King Edward VII to Scilly.

Lime Burning

The strongly acid soils of Cornwall, though very suitable for the propagation of rhododendrons and azaleas in her parks and gardens, need lime for successful husbandry. Sometimes this lime was applied to the land in the form of shelley-sand (p 130) and indeed the *Handbook for Travellers* (1865) states, apropos the sand at the entrance of the Camel estuary:

The sands are thought to be now on the decrease owing to the amazing quantity which is annually taken from the Dunbar (the Doom Bar sandbank off Trebetherick) and dispatched for manure up the country. They are said to be the richest in the county in carbonate of lime, and are in such demand that the amount thus carried away in the year is no less than 100000 tons.

The railway had barely developed in Cornwall at this time, and there was a constant trade carried on by small coastal ships bringing, as ballast, limestone from quarries near Plymouth and from others at Aberthaw on the Glamorgan coast to be burnt in local Cornish kilns and there made into lime, both for building and agriculture. Michael Tangye's *The History of Portreath* records that a kiln existed there in 1753, some years before the new harbour was started in 1760.

These small ships were able to penetrate the furthest depths of the many creeks in the Cornish estuaries, and the remains of old kilns can be found in remote locations like Little Petherick on the Camel Estuary and Ruan Lanihorne Quay on the tiny Ruan River, which empties its water into the Fal nearby and which today is almost totally silted up due to clay washing upstream. The presence of this kiln is a witness to the former maritime activity of this tiny village. Another kiln is to be found at the head of Pont Pill, a creek on the east side of the Fowey estuary in Lanteglos parish and now in National Trust hands. It is to be hoped that, in such ownership, the value of such remains to students of industrial history will be recognised, unlike the case of the eighteenth-century kiln at Portreath destroyed in 1967 to provide a building site. There are also two large kilns at Lerryn, an old port at the head of a long creek on the Fowey River, and a range of four at St Blazey alongside the Treffry Canal. At Hayle, on Carnsew Quay within the extensive property belonging to Harvey & Co Ltd was a handsome circular building containing two kilns, and probably unique of its kind in Cornwall. It was destroyed in the 1950s.

The production of the lime was effected by building a fire of wood and coal at the bottom of the kiln. Some burners would kindle it, then throw the limestone on to the red hot embers from the roof, alternating layers of coal and lime until the kiln was full. Another method was to build up the entire kiln cold and then fire it from the bottom. The final product was extracted from the bottom of the kiln.

THE GAS INDUSTRY

It is fitting, in this chapter, to record briefly the development of the gas industry for this started in Cornwall in the eighteenth century, and played a considerable part in domestic life as well as in industry.

William Murdoch, born at Bello Mill in Ayrshire in 1754, came south in 1777 to work in Matthew Boulton's foundry at Soho, Birmingham. Two years later, he became manager of Boulton's branch office in Redruth, and became interested in the uses of coal, taking out a patent for dyestuffs extracted from coal in 1791. He was thus a pioneer of aniline dyes. The following year, at his office-home in Cross Street, he publicly demonstrated the efficiency of using coal gas as an illuminant. The furthest burner was 70ft from the primitive cast-iron vertical retort and it was the first practical application in Cornwall of coal-gas lighting. A decade later, in 1802, the Peace of Amiens was celebrated by the illumination of the Soho Foundry by gas, the installation having been designed by him. It is almost certain that Cornwall's first gasworks was constructed at the Perran Foundry at the very beginning of the nineteenth century for it is known that these works produced gas not only for the foundry itself but also for piping to houses and cottages in the village. The first street to be lit with gas was Pall Mall in London in 1812.

Cornwall, so dynamic an industrial area at this period, was quick to realise the value of this new form of energy and between 1817, when the first gas lamps began to illuminate the streets of Falmouth, and the end of the century, twenty-six separate undertakings were formed to provide gas for domestic purposes, public lighting and for business and industry from Calstock to St Just in Penwith.

The earliest gasworks to be built were in Falmouth, Helston, and Redruth, all by 1830, in which year the first gasworks was opened in Penzance. In the next decade, Launceston, Liskeard and St Ives works were opened. In 1842, the Oatey & Martin Foundry in Wadebridge began to manufacture gas for the townspeople, an example which was followed by the Holman Foundry at St Just in 1860; meanwhile, in the fifties, Lostwithiel and Penryn works had been opened. The sixties saw gas supplied to the towns of Bodmin, Looe, Padstow, Saltash and St Columb Major, all before 1870, to be followed in the seventies by Callington, Gunnislake, Camborne, Newquay and St Austell.

The final twenty years of the century saw works established at Torpoint in 1884, the incorporation of the Hayle Gas Company in 1889 (although gas had been manufactured at the Hayle Foundry years before) and finally at Fowey and St Blazey. In the twentieth century, the Bude Gas Works was opened in 1908. All gas undertakings were nationalised in May 1949 and vested in the South Western Gas Board. What was said to be the last hand-fired gas-making plant in England, ended its days at the Torpoint Works on 30 September 1969, and when gas making ceased at Bude in May 1970, it ceased entirely in Cornwall, where it had originated 180 years before.

There is, however, one further Cornish town that has a special place in this survey since the lighting of its streets and houses was, almost uniquely, with acetylene gas. Mr C. E. Leese, who was headmaster of Camelford Grammar School from 1918, has contributed this note:

The Camelford Acetylene Gas Co Ltd was started some years before the first World War to provide gas for domestic and street lighting only. A number of local people took up shares. The production of the gas, at its peak half a century ago, was by dripping water on to calcium carbide and storing the gas under pressure in a small gasholder. It was a messy affair subject to chokage and throwing out large quantities of slaked lime as a by-product. This was initially used in agriculture and by local builders, but it was unsuitable in the one and a menace in the other because of sulphurous and other impurities. The acetylene flame produced gave a high intensity of light but it was very sensitive to any reduction in the oxygen supply and disposed to choke burners and to produce clouds of black smoke! In the late 30s the local Electricity Undertaking 'invaded' Camelford, took over street lighting and almost at once the acetylene production ceased. The plant, which was on the site of Chapel Cottage, a post Reformation house, itself built on the site of a chapel built in 1311 and dedicated to St Thomas of Canterbury was for many years in the charge of Mr Samuel Coombe. He was also the official lamp-lighter a job he performed with much dignity!

The first public building in Cornwall believed to have been illuminated with carbide gas was Mount Hawke Wesleyan Chapel in 1906. The engineer was William Plummer of Mount Hawke.

ELECTRICITY

The brief history of electricity supply throughout Cornwall spans a period of forty years, commencing in 1886 when, following the use of electrical energy in the china-clay industry, a works was built in St Austell by Veale & Co Ltd. This private undertaking was taken over by the St Austell & District Electric Lighting & Power Co Ltd in 1900 supplying power in St Austell urban and rural districts. The Borough of Fowey was added in 1927 when a diesel generating station was built at Pont's Mill, Tywardreath. Near St Austell the small fishing port of Mevagissey had its own local supply as early as 1896, a fact which has given rise to the statement that it was the first place in Britain to have electric lighting in its streets. The honour, however, goes to Godalming in Surrey, where the first electric street lamps were lit in 1881.

The mining industry of Camborne and Redruth first began to look at electric power in the nineties, and in 1899 the first electricity order was obtained for Camborne, the idea being to use water-power from a stream in the Polstrong area west of the town. These proposals did not rouse sufficient interest, and the Urban Electric Supply Company took over the order and obtained from the Board of Trade further orders extending the distribution area to Illogan and Redruth. A generating station was completed at Carn Brea in 1902 of 425kW capacity provided by four Bellis & Morcom steam generators. This company also constructed and ran Cornwall's only electric tramway which ran between the two towns of Camborne and Redruth from 1902 to 1927 (plate, p 125). The increasing use of electrical power in this populous industrial district put too heavy a load on the Carn Brea station and in 1910 it was decided to build a larger one on a new site where there was plenty of condensing water as well as facilities for a seaborne coal supply. The Hayle Generating Station was opened the following year, continuing to this day.

Falmouth had its electricity supply from the Electric Supply Corporation starting in December 1906, in which year the Newquay Electric Light & Power Co Ltd built a steam generating station at Mount Wise to supply that town. Further up the coast, the Wadebridge & District Electric Supply Co Ltd and the Bude Electric Supply Co commenced their generation and supply in 1908; to be followed in 1912 by a supply to Padstow provided from the iceworks of the North Cornwall Ice & Cold Storage Co. Padstow was then an important port for herring and mackerel and the thirty to forty trawlers operating from the harbour needed considerable quantities of ice.

The year 1911 saw the formation of the Launceston & District Electric Supply Co using Crossley gas engines, and in October of the following year electricity came to Penzance from the new Hayle Station supplying power to the Penzance & District Electric Supply Co Ltd. In 1913, the Old Delabole Slate Co offered to supply power to the village and the plant, mains and services were installed by W. G. Heath & Co of Plymouth for £1,284, completed January 1914. During World War I, in 1915, this same company commenced to supply the towns of Saltash and Torpoint. The 1920s first saw the formation of the Bodmin Electric Light & Supply Co Ltd in 1920, in which year, a water-powered generator was installed to supply Penryn by the Penryn Electric Supply Co, later augmented by an oil engine. Looe Electricity Co Ltd was registered in 1926 to acquire the electrical engineering business of Roberts & Co who had been supplying the town since 1924.

The last three places to obtain electricity were Callington, where the Callington & District Electric Supply Co commenced in March 1925; Liskeard, where the Liskeard Gas & Electricity Co Ltd started in December 1925 and finally Truro, where the town did not obtain electricity until 1927 from the Truro Electricity Supply Co Ltd, taking bulk supply from the Cornwall Electric Power Company. The rationalising of the electric supply industry, together with the rural electrification scheme 1929–35, brought about the Cornwall Electric Power Act of 1936 when ten local companies were transferred to the Cornwall Electric Power Co, which was itself transferred to the South Western Electricity Board in 1948.

BREWING

In late Elizabethan times, Richard Carew recorded that:

> Barley is growne into great use of late yeeres so as now they till a larger quantitie in one Hundred, than was in the whole Shire before. This increase of Barley tillage hath also amended the Cornish drinke, by converting that gaine into Mault which (to the ill relishing of strangers) in former times they made onely of Oates.

Later on in his *Survey*, when writing of the 'Cornishmens recreations', he describes harvest dinners and church-ales.

> For the Church-ale, two young men of the parish are yerely chosen to be Wardens who, dividing the task, make collection among the parishioners of whatsoever provision it pleaseth them to bestow. This they imploy in brewing and baking against Whitsontide.

This ancient industry of brewing contains a wealth of fascinating buildings in the field of industrial archaeology all over the country, but, as in so many industries, the concentration of brewing in a few large establishments has meant a considerable destruction of historic breweries, particularly during the past twenty years. In the middle of the nineteenth century, when the population of Cornwall had reached its peak, *Slater's Commercial Directory* (1852) recorded twelve separate breweries in the county. Robert Allen's in Killigrew Street, Falmouth; James Clark's and Ellis & Co's, both in Helston; Dodd &

Tresidder's Brewery in Quay Road, Penryn; and the Ponsanooth Brewery owned by John Hart. Edwin Polkinghorne's Mounts Bay Brewery, Christopher Stephen's in Market Jew Street and Stephen Weaver's in North Street, were all in Penzance. Redruth had its brewery operated by Magor, Davey & Co; Samuel Moyle's was at Chacewater; while John Short's and William Rundle's were both at Saltash on the Tamar.

Half a century ago, there were seven: Bowhay & Bros at Albaston near Gunnislake, a small brewery that closed about 1920; Moyle's in Station Road, Chacewater; Christopher Ellis's Brewery near St Elwyn's Church, Hayle; Carne's 'screw-top' brewery in Market Street, Falmouth, that was demolished to make way for the Odeon Cinema about 1935 (the firm merged with Devenish); Venning's Steam Brewery in Liskeard, closed in recent years when the brewery was bought out by the Watney Group; and Hicks' Brewery in St Austell. A small local brewery that lingered on until about 1943 was the Treluswell on the Truro road leading out of Penryn; the old building is still extant. In the 1880s it was run by the Hart family in conjunction with the Ponsanooth Brewery. In Penzance there was also the Angle Brewing Co in Parade Street which had only a short life.

Only two breweries, existing in 1919, are still extant in Cornwall: the brewery at Redruth owned by Devenish Redruth Brewery Ltd, which is known to have existed on the same site since before 1827 (and where there is still steam power); and the brewery at St Austell established in 1860 by the Hicks family, now the St Austell Brewery Co. This brewery has existed on the present site since 1891. Of interest, however, is the small brewery that exists at the Blue Anchor Inn in Coinage Hall Street, Helston, since brewing has been operated on this site for probably five centuries. It is believed to be the only brewery of its type, ie in an inn, in the west of England and it represents the last of what were common enough a century or more ago. The brewer is Mr Geoffrey Richards.

Associated with this trade are maltings and it is not so very many years since barges were towed up the Fal and Truro rivers to anchor on the north side of Lemon Quay (now occupied by the city car park) to discharge their cargo into the Devenish cellars under the Mansion House in Princes Street. After unloading, the barges would be towed downstream to Malpas and up the Tresillian river to the extensive maltings on the north bank of the creek, some of which are still visible; one conical ventilator still exists as a reminder of the days of local breweries and their needs, and the ship-borne trade that supplied them.

FISHING

In the *Survey of Cornwall* (1602) Richard Carew describes in some detail the method of fishing peculiar to Cornwall by the use of the long net which he calls 'the sayne':

> Three or foure boates lie hovering off upon the coast directed by a Balker or Huer standing on the Cliffe side, who best discerneth the course of the Pilchard and cundeth the Master of each boate by crying with a loud voice, and wheazing diversified and significant signes with a bush in his hand.

After the huge shoal had been landed:

> Those which are to bee ventred for France they pack in staunch hogsheads so to keep them in their pickle. Those that serve for the hotter countries of Spaine and Italie they fume in a house building for the nonce, drying them with the smoake of a soft and continual fire.

Three and a half centuries later this trade was still being carried on, nearly 122 million pilchards being packed in 40,880 hogsheads in 1847. In 1850, almost exactly the same description of seine fishing (the Cornish word 'sayn', or 'sayne' as used by Carew, had now become anglicised) was given in the *Handbook for Travellers in Devon and Cornwall*; indeed, in that year, with the trade at full prosperity, a lugger was built at Polperro large enough to carry seine nets, 1,400 fathoms in length, over 1½ miles. In 1860, £80,000 worth of fish of various kinds was sent to London and other markets and fifteen to twenty years later, about 400 boats were at work landing about 4,000

M

tons of fish per season. At the peak there were about 500 boats operating from Cornish ports, including visitors from the East Coast, principally Yarmouth and Lowestoft. In three months between March and May 1905, £168,000 of fish was landed at Newlyn alone and, because of an overloaded market, 50,000 fish were thrown back in the sea. In May 1905, the enormous pilchard shoal extended over a distance of 100 miles!

The pilchard industry resulted in the building of 'fish cellars' at many places along the coast—the 'houses' that Carew had noted in Elizabethan times. Here the fish were packed in layers with salt and then pressed down with weights to extract the oil, an operation of two to three weeks duration. About 1900, this age-old practice was changed when fish were packed in vats or large tanks with salt, left for three weeks until pickled and then the pressing to extract the oil started. Little wonder that travellers to the Cornish fishing towns in the nineteenth century, indeed in the early years of this, wrote 'they are best viewed from a distance' (said of Padstow in the *Handbook for Travellers*) or, as a visitor to Portreath described in *The History of Portreath*: 'we used to witness pilchards cured in long sheds, women standing on the unctuous floor, salting and laying them up in heaps to drain. The odour was unutterable!'

The industry gave rise to employment for many: in boat building and sailmaking requiring sail lofts and shipyards; in net manufacture, often a cottage industry, and net barking; and in the establishment in many places of ice works. About the turn of this century, hundreds of boats were working out of ports from Polperro to Newlyn and St Ives to Port Isaac. But the huge export trade was not to last for ever. Over the later years there was a decreasing demand for what must have been, at best, a pretty unpleasant fish by the time it was extracted from the cask, and the last great shoal of pilchards, esti-mated at 3 million fish, was taken off Porthgwarra near Land's End in 1916, realising £4,500. Over a period of forty years, 500 boats dwindled to a mere half dozen.

The late Claude Berry wrote in *Cornwall* (1963):

. . . the sad symbolism of the decaying fish cellars all around the Cornish coast with the great decline of the fishing industry, leaving in its wake from Cawsand to Newlyn to Port Gaverne, grey crumbling buildings over the portals of which a mason might well have inscribed a sad 'Hic jacet'. Indeed a mason did one such on a fish cellar at Harlyn Bay near Catacleuse Quarry Padstow.

Berry, too, echoes those Victorian travellers:

> The rank smell of the pilchard industry must have pervaded every nook and cranny of the cellar, the courtyard, the salt stores and the lofts. This was no place for those with delicate nostrils and sensitive stomachs.

Off the main road from Par to Fowey, a narrow lane leads to Menabilly, with an even narrower one down to the coast at the old fishing cove of Polkerris. At the south end of the beach there is a long curved pier, built mainly of slate and started in 1740 by the Rashleigh family of Menabilly. Near the shore-end of the pier are the well-preserved remains of a large two-chambered lime-kiln and, close by, the archaeological remains of what has been described as the largest fish cellar in Cornwall. This long two-storeyed building has an open courtyard running down the centre and the remnants of once substantial stone columns supporting the lofts.

In the 1870s, it was recorded that the pilchard industry was established here by the Rashleighs, and it operated successfully for many years: but 'has declined latterly'. This cellar at Polkerris is an excellent example of those 'grey crumbling buildings' described by Claude Berry, a remnant of a once great export industry that not only employed great numbers of men and women all around the coast, but which provided many poor people with a staple diet, at ten fish for one penny!

In several places too, notably St Ives and Newquay, there survives an old Huer's hut, another remnant of the pilchard industry. The Newquay one is whitewashed and located on the headland, having an outer stairway and a little tower. From it, the huer, having spotted the pilchard shoal, would cry 'Hevra! Hevra!' (the Cornish word for shoaling) and all would be bustle and go, the inhabitants rushing from their houses and the seine boats flying in pursuit of the precious fish.

The growth of the fishing industry was primarily responsible for several new and improved harbours in Cornwall during the eighteenth and nineteenth centuries, in particular Mevagissey, Newlyn, Padstow, Porthleven, Polperro and St Ives, and the small refuges of Portscatho, Coverack, Mullion and Sennen. Details of these harbours are found on page 142 and in the Gazetteer.

SHIPBUILDING AND ASSOCIATED TRADES

The fishing industry, coupled with maritime trading, gave rise to the building of small sailing ships, smacks, ketches and schooners, in a number of shipyards along the coast-line and in the creeks of Cornish rivers. They were the maids of all work, those small merchant ships, carrying cargoes from small harbour to small harbour, up into the furthest recesses of long creeks such as Lerryn and Tresillian, taking cargoes even from farm to farm. They plied between tiny roadside quays like Bishop's Quay on the Helford River and small coastal harbours such as Gorran Haven. They sailed up the Tamar to Cotehele Quay or to Morwellham with lime, up the Lynher River to St Germans to load roadstone, and they collected cargoes of oysters from the Truro River, trading in any sort of commodity that would yield a small profit.

A century ago, Kelly's *Directory* (1873) recorded forty-three ship-builders and shipwrights, among them Hugh Stephens of Devoran who built the *Mary* of Truro in 1875, Charles Dyer who built the *Mystery* of Truro, launched a decade later at Sunny Corner, Malpas, on the Truro River, and John Stephens (brother of Hugh) who worked from Yard Point near Devoran, then a thriving port. At Calstock, underneath the tall railway viaduct, was the famous Goss shipyard whose last ship was the *Garlandstone* (1909) whilst at Padstow, John Cowl launched the 88ft pitch-pine schooner, the *Katie* in 1881. This ship, 'the last engineless cargo schooner in Europe' according to *The Times* of 4 August 1971, is lying in Copenhagen Docks and a Preservation Society has been launched to bring her back to her native Cornwall. This ship used to carry, inter alia, pilchard cargoes from Cornish ports to the Mediterranean.

Another famous Cornish shipbuilder was Henry Trethowan of Falmouth and Flushing who built a famous three-masted schooner, the *Mary Barrow* in 1891; a frequent visitor to Penzance in the 1920s and 1930s, bringing in cement and taking away china clay. She was lost without trace in 1938. The Clemens Brothers of Newquay were responsible for building many of the ships there during the forty years 1840–80.

The last of the sailing ships to trade at Cornish ports were the *Kathleen and May* (1900) and the *Result* (1893), both of which have been saved from the breaker's yard in recent years, the former by the Maritime Trust.

Associated with the industry of shipbuilding were the trades of ropemaker and sailmaker; Kelly's *Directory* (1873) listing no fewer than 37 ropemakers and 25 sailmakers but, curiously enough, only 1 net manufacturer, Benjamin Eddy of Porthleven. The decline of these industries is indicated in the entries in Kelly's *Directory* for 1935 which listed only two ropemakers, one in Launceston (see Gazetteer) and one in Mevagissey; four sailmakers; one shipwright at Malpas and four shipbuilders, one of which was the Little Falmouth Yacht Yard where Trethowan built his schooners in Victorian times.

In the days when huge quantities of fish, china clay and arsenic were shipped in barrels, the cooper was an important craftsman in the community. The *Directory* for 1873 records the names of 54 coopers and the Truro Cooperage Co under John Tregoning's managership in Quay Street. By 1906 the number had dropped to 19, to 10 by 1930 and to only 7 by 1935, of whom 4 were in St Austell, 1 in Lostwithiel, 1 in Looe and 1 in Gunnislake.

BRICKMAKING

Cornwall, a county that abounds in so many varieties of building

stone, has never been noted for its brick buildings, such as are found
for example in East Anglia and the Home Counties. The brickmaking
industry in the county did, however, make its contribution over a
period of about a century after 1850. Perhaps the earliest known
works at this period is the Lizard Brick & Tile Works, 1851–67,
started at the suggestion of the Hon A. M. Agar of Lanhydrock in
order to supply clay drainage pipes for wet land. The coal for the kiln
came from South Wales and was landed at Church Cove, Landewednack. Extensive details can be found in the *Journals of the Lizard
Field Club* for 1963 and 1965, compiled by Miss Ruth Phillips.

   The china-clay industry, following the success of the large brickworks at Lee Moor in Devon, produced yellow bricks for the building
industry as well as firebricks at several places in Cornwall, notably
the Burthy Brick Works at St Enoder from about 1880; the West of
England Brick Works at Goonamarris, St Stephen-in-Brannel; and
the Carbis Brick Works at Roche which were in operation until about
1941. These works often produced as well the flat tiles needed for the
china-clay dries. In West Cornwall, in the parishes of Germoe and
Breage, traditionally the site where William Cookworthy first discovered 'kaolin', William Argall operated the Wheal Grey and the
Tregoning Brick Works during the eighties; 6 miles to the north-west
on the Marazion Marshes, Richard Williams was making bricks at
Newtown also in this same decade. At Redruth, adjoining the Ped'n-
an-Drea Mine, the 1877 Ordnance Survey clearly shows a Crucible
Works and Kelly's *Directory* of 1873 carries an advertisement of
'John Juleff Cornish Plumbago Crucible Maker for Tin Assaying'
and Richard Juleff brickmaker.

   In the far north, Edward Rudland of Red Post, Launcells, which
was on the Bude Canal, advertised as a brickmaker during the
eighties, perhaps as a successor to the Launcells Brick & Tile Company of 1873. Precisely 2 miles due south, on the railway, and half a
mile west of the old LSWR Whitstone & Bridgerule station, are the
derelict remains of the North Cornwall Brick Company's Works, in
operation until about 1950.

The most important brickmaking parish in Cornwall was undoubtedly Calstock and details can be found in the Gazetteer (pp 213–14) of the remains of the extensive brick, terra cotta and firebrick works at Cox Park, Hingston Down, Chilsworthy and Gunnislake that were in operation between about 1852 and 1939.

Prior to the building of the Royal Victualling Yard in Devonport (completed in 1835), the Royal Navy had a brewery known as the 'king's brewhouse' at Southdown on the north shore of Millbrook Lake a mile west of Mount Edgcumbe. It was owned by the Victualling Commissioners to the Navy. After 1835, there was for a time a smelter on the site, but by 1883 the South Western Brick Company had established a brickworks there. On the 1914 Ordnance Survey, a circular kiln 90ft in diameter appears, and adjoining it a narrow rectangular kiln 150ft in length. The clay quarry that supplied the raw material covered 5½ acres in 1914 and 10 acres in 1950 and the works undoubtedly used ships to transport its products since the Southdown Quay adjoins it. Three separate undertakings were in operation in 1935: the Southdown Brick Works, the Devonshire Brick Works and the South Western Brick Works, all owned by the Western Counties Brick Company Ltd. They were operational in 1950 but had become derelict by about 1961 and were razed to the ground in the winter of 1967.

The only other place of note is Par where John Alderman made bricks in the first fifteen years of this century and where Treffry, Clunes & Co were also listed as brickmakers up to 1935, latterly under the name of Clunes & Co.

EXPLOSIVES AND FUSES

In *Observations on the West of England Mining Region* J. H. Collins quotes from Robert Hunt's *British Mining* that it was at the Great Wheal Vor in Breage parish that gunpowder was first used in Cornish mining. The date is generally believed to be about 1689, because the parish register in Breage contains an entry as follows:

Thomas Epsley of Chilcumpton (Sumersetshere) hee was the man that
brought the rare invention of shooting the rocks, which came here in June
1689, and was buried at Breague the 16th day of December 1689!

A factory that was established early in the nineteenth century in
Cornwall for the manufacture of explosives was the East Cornwall
Gunpowder Works located in the bottom of a deep and secluded
valley $5\frac{1}{2}$ miles north-west of Looe. In John Allen's *History of
Liskeard* (1856) he states that:

> . . . an undertaking which owed its origins to the mines was the East
> Cornwall Gunpowder Company, established in 1846 at Herodsfoot. It has
> supplied large quantities of powder to this and other districts, and does an
> extensive business. An explosion in 1850 caused the deaths of two workmen.

There is a local legend that black powder for the Navy at the time of
the Battle of Trafalgar was made at Herodsfoot, the woodlands of the
district providing the charcoal. By 1906 the Herodsfoot Mills were
producing Ammotal, the company being known as Ammonal Explosives Ltd, their product having been invented by a colliery explosives expert, a Mr Weizman. The Directories over the period
1914–30 disclose no information about explosives being made here,
but in 1914, another explosives mill was in operation at Trago Mills
in the Glynn Valley between Bodmin Road and Doublebois stations.
In 1914, it was operated by Morpal Ltd, and five years later by the
Blastine Explosives Co. About 1931, Messrs F. R. & J. G. Burrows
of Liskeard, whose father had been a foreman at Trago Mills, formed
another company to manufacture an explosive 'Burrowite' and in
1938, the war being imminent, they decided to make TNT. A new
plant was built at Trago and a Mr Herbert Wilson, an experienced
chemist in the explosives industry (and father of a future Prime
Minister) joined the firm as general manager. During the war years,
military Burrowite was made at Herodsfoot and at Trago Mills under
Mr Wilson's managership.

The end of explosives manufacture came at Herodsfoot on Sunday,
23 June 1963, when there was an explosion at the mill causing one
death. Soon afterwards the company sold the works to ICI together

with Trago Mills which had only been used as a magazine since about 1945. ICI kept Herodsfoot as an explosives store until about 1966. A large derelict waterwheel is still extant at Herodsfoot and there are the remains of the old tramway tracks along the valley bottom that once echoed with the clang of trucks. The valley sides are now clothed with pine forests and the whole place has an air of mystery about it.

There is always an element of danger in the manufacture of explosives, hence these establishments were often sited in remote valleys. In the parish of St Allen, the Cornwall Blasting Powder Works was in operation a century ago on a similar site to Herodsfoot. This was a deep wooded valley known as Bishop's Wood, $2\frac{1}{2}$ miles due north of Truro. There is, however, no reference to this firm in the eighties.

The main road (A393) that links Redruth with Penryn runs through the village of Ponsanooth, 3 miles north-west of Penryn. Flowing through this steep valley in a north-easterly direction is the Kennal River whose swiftly flowing stream provided water-power for several industries in the last century. In 1873, the Kennal Gunpowder Company, who were manufacturers of gunpowder and saltpetre refiners, had established their works in the vale and they continued in business at least until 1906 when they became a part of Curtis's & Harvey who had incorporated the East Cornwall works at Herodsfoot. Curtis's & Harvey continued until the later thirties when they were represented at Ponsanooth by Bickford Smith & Co Ltd (pp 202–3).

The sole survivor today in the vale is the ICI gutta-percha works, which has important links with the explosives industry since gutta-percha is used to cover fuses, and is of interest to the industrial historian since its steam power is provided by a distinctive Cornish boiler (pioneered by Trevithick) bearing the plate 'R. Visick. Devoran', a firm still in being in that place.

Before Perranporth on the north coast of Cornwall was opened up for the tourist with the building of the Newquay–Chacewater branch of the GWR in 1903–5, it was another remote place mainly concerned

with mining. Here about eighty years ago, the British & Colonial
Explosives Co Ltd established their factory on the cliffs at the
southern end of Perran Beach, storing their products for safety in dry
caves and old mine workings. They became part of Nobel's Explosives Company early in this century and continued at Perranporth
until about 1920.

Fifteen miles further south-west another large explosives factory
was established in 1889 by the National Explosives Company, later
the National Dynamite Company, covering a site of 200 acres on the
extensive sand dunes called Upton Towans north-east of Hayle.
There was an explosion of considerable magnitude at these works
during World War I and they closed down entirely c 1919. The site
is still, however, used by ICI Ltd.

Much of the products of the Cornish explosives manufacturies was
shipped from the quay at Penryn, but in recent times Bickford Smith/
ICI used the old Lelant quay on the estuary of the Hayle River for
this purpose.

Associated with the explosives industry is the allied trade of fuse-
making, indeed the first man to patent a safety fuse was a Cornish
leather merchant William Bickford of Illogan in 1831. For a long
time, rushes and goose quills were used to hold the gunpowder in situ
since the rush or quill burnt slowly and so gave the miners a chance
to get clear. But inevitably there were many serious accidents, and
Bickford is credited with getting the idea of a fuse when observing
rope spinning. On the former Bickford Smith/ICI fuse factory in
Tuckingmill near Camborne there is a cast-tin plaque to the inventor,
to whom a patent was granted on 6 September 1831. Kelly's *Directory*
(1873) carries an advertisement of Bickford, Smith & Co stating that
they had won prize medals at various exhibitions since 1851, and
stating that they were the original patentees of the 'Patent Safety Fuse
for conveying Fire to the Charge in Blasting Rocks'. Their patent was
two separate threads passing through the column of gunpowder in
every coil.

At that period there was competition in this field of work, for

William Bennetts, at one time an engineer with Bickford, had also established a fuse factory near Tuckingmill and was a keen rival of the original company. Alfred Lanyon, proprietor of the Redruth Gas Works, established the British & Foreign Safety Fuse Company at Plain-an-Gwary, Redruth; William Brunton & Co had their 'safety' fuse factory at Pool between the two towns, whilst at Tregullow, Scorrier, the Williams family of Scorrier House established the Unity Patent Safety Fuse Company. In 1907, Bickford Smith & Co acquired control of Bennetts Sons & Co on the death of the owner, but both factories, one at Tuckingmill, the other nearby at Roskear, continued until 1924. Bickford Smith also bought out the Unity Company at Tregullow and this factory was subsequently closed. There was another fuse factory in Foundry Row, Redruth, managed by a Mr J. H. Hoyden who also sold his interests in fusemaking to Bickford Smith in 1907, but fuses continued to be made here until 1914.

After World War I, Bickford Smith & Co Ltd were the sole makers of safety fuses in Cornwall, their main factory being at Tuckingmill with a smaller unit at Ponsanooth in the Kennal Vale, to which had been transferred the gutta-percha processing plant c 1917. Bickford Smith & Co Ltd joined the merger of Explosives Trades Ltd in 1918 which successively became Nobel Industries and then Imperial Chemical Industries Ltd (ICI).

A further industry connected with fuses was that of tape manufacture and, in Kennel Vale, Bickford Smith operated a factory for this purpose up to 1914. This was in all probability the factory of E. & S. Polkinghorn used for the manufacture of flannel and serge a century or so ago.

PART TWO

Gazetteer

MANY of the sites mentioned in Part One are included in this gazetteer; but so prolific were the industries of Cornwall that it has been impossible to list all the remains and for some areas a selection of the more outstanding has had to be made. The gazetteer includes many sites which have not previously been mentioned.

The grid references are based on the Ordnance Survey one-inch scale sheets for Cornwall, ie sheet numbers 174, 185–7, 189 and 190.

ANTONY

A curiosity is the remains of the Cornish Military Railway, built in late-Victorian times. When Palmerston was Prime Minister (1855–65) he was deeply concerned about a possible attack by the French on Devonport Dockyard. Forts were constructed, two of which were Scraesdon at Antony and Tregantle on the cliffs above Whitsand Bay. In 1890 Royal Engineers began to construct a special 4ft 8½in gauge railway from a new quay at Wacker Lake on the Lynher River to Tregantle Fort; completed three years later, 2½ miles long. From Wacker Pier there was a cable incline up a gradient of 1 in 7 to Scraesdon Fort, then the railway climbed to the summit at Berry Green before running in to the batteries at Tregantle Down (186/389532). Its main purpose was to convey heavy 9in shells for the Tregantle Ordnance but it also transported water and victuals. When the War Office withdrew the 9in guns from the battery about 1904 the railway came to an end, but it was not finally taken up until 1916 and one of the locomotives remained in its shed at Wacker Quay (186/390550) until about 1933. A few traces remain today: the old bridge under highway A38 west of Antony, and some of the old flat-bottomed rails around Tregantle used as target guides and trench revetments.

ASHTON

Ashton was once the centre of a thriving copper, tin and china-clay industry:

1   At 189/558293 east of the road that leads from the Falmouth Packet Inn to Prussia Cove lies the cracked engine house of Wheal Speedwell copper mine.

2   At 189/580289 in a caravan site south of Germoe crossroads rise the two chimney stacks of a group of copper mines known as the Great Western.

3   At 189/595291 are the engine house and stacks of Wheal Grey. Its history is bound up with the two hills that rise behind it, Tregoning Hill and Tresowes Hill, for it was nearby that William Cookworthy about 1745 discovered kaolin and petuntse and first exploited them. It would be difficult to locate the exact site of Cookworthy's workings, but many pits are to be found in the neighbourhood and especially on the top of Tregoning Hill. In 1878 the winning of tin and clay came under a single operation when Will Argall of Breage and John Toy of Helston acquired the Wheal Grey China-Clay & Tin Company. They also built brickkilns one of which can still be seen on the northern slope of Tregoning Hill at 189/606299.

4   In the saddle between Tregoning Hill and Godolphin Hill are the engine house of Great Work (189/596307) and the remains of Wheal Vreath (189/590307). It is believed that the first Newcomen engine was installed here.

BALDHU

The thriving mining industry, particularly in the period between 1840 and 1900, accounted for the creation of this new parish in 1847, Lord Falmouth erecting a new church for the community the following year at 190/772432. The area, lonely and windswept, abounds in old mine workings, particularly those associated with Wheal Jane and associated mines, which became the Falmouth Consolidated Mines in 1907. Will this become an important mining area again with the new Janes Mine?

BISSOE

Near 190/777414 and along the banks of the river to Twelveheads is an important industrial complex in miniature. Among the many ruins will be found: ochre pits; copper precipitation works; a small iron foundry; the chemical works of William Conn, founded about 1850; the Cornwall Arsenic Works; the Bissoe Chemical Manure & Vitriol Works, owned in 1873 by John Paynter; the Bissoe Bridge Smelting Co works, at one time operated by C. K. Vigurs of Penzance; and the tin smelting works of the Tregonings, a Gwennap family who in 1851 established their own tin-plate works in Llanelly. Beyond Conn's chemical works and to the north-west is the engine house of the Nangiles Mine and the mouth of the County Adit, a complicated system of drainage tunnels constructed in the eighteenth century to unwater the Gwennap mines.

BLISLAND

Noteworthy for its great 50ft waterwheel at 186/112734, known as the Gawns or Durfold wheel. Originally made in 1865 by the Hawarden Iron Works in Flintshire, and shipped to the Isle of Man for pumping at the Laxey silver mines, it was dismantled and brought to Wadebridge by rail in 1920, and then hauled to Durfold by traction engine and erected. Almost unbelievably, as it turned it operated a flat-rod over a *distance of* 1¼ *miles*, at the extremity of which there was a 14in pump at Parkyn's clay works at Temple on Bodmin Moor (189/135732).

Close by Tresarrett Wharf at 189/090730 is Lavethan Corn Mill, now one of the last two water-powered mills in continuous use in Cornwall, a relic of 300 working mills recorded in 1883. The wheel, all metal and 15ft diameter was made in 1921 at Wadebridge.

N

At various places in the vicinity of Blisland are unique milestones, consisting of square granite shafts of various heights with a large granite capstone bearing the names of various towns and villages carved on the faces. The tallest has a shaft about 8ft high and is to be found at 185/073775 on highway B3266.

BODMIN

The original Bodmin Wharf station of the B&WR built sometime after 1834 and the LSWR station (1894) at 185/069672 have both gone, but the GWR station of 1887 is still extant at St Nicholas (185/072664). At 185/074675 are the gaunt stone buildings of the 1842 workhouse; and at 185/065675 adjoining the former LSWR railway track, the macabre near-ruins of the great prison, erected 'from designs of Mr Potter London, Architect' in the late 1850s on approximately the same site as the earlier gaol built 1778–80. The enterprising B&WR brought 1,100 people from Wadebridge on 13 April 1840 in three special trains to view the public execution of William and James Lightfoot outside this gaol beside their railway. Two great ornamental iron gates from this prison, sold after it was auctioned in 1927, are now to be seen at Mill Garage, Blackwater, on A30 (190/725447).

An elegant Victorian bank building is to be found at Barclays premises 7 Mount Folly adjoining the Assize Courts; originally the East Cornwall Bank and later absorbed by Barclays.

Coincident with the great rise in the population of Cornwall during the first half of the century, were great improvements in agriculture. In Fore Street, the extensive cattle market, its façade decorated with sculptured heads of bulls and rams and opened in 1844 is good solid industrial architecture.

BOSCASTLE

Within the parish of Forrabury & Minster and described as late as the 1930s as 'a small seaport town'. The harbour (174/100915), originally c 1540, is like a fiord. It was used for centuries by sailing schooners trading in corn, Cornish roofing slate, tanning bark and, for a time, china clay. Coal and limestone were exported.

BREAGE

Near this village of sturdily built miners' cottages and the houses of mine captains are the sites of four mines of importance:

1 Great Wheal Vor (189/621302), one of Cornwall's richest and oldest tin mines. Worked originally by the Godolphin family, it was here that gunpowder was reputed to have been first used and the first steam pumping-engine installed. In its heyday it prided itself on using some of the county's most famed engines: Crease's 100in; Borlase's 100in and Trelawney's 85in, both built by Harveys of Hayle with Hocking & Loam as engineers; Arthur Woolf's 53in and two man-engines. Now it is a scene of desolation. Even its own smelter has gone, its name perpetuated in Smelter Shaft 200yd east of Carleen village at 189/619301.

2 Wheal Metal (189/629299) where a massive engine house still remains.

3 Scott's Mine (189/622295) with its engine house, two buddles in excellent condition, water tanks, a fine calciner stack with its top ornamented in rich red-brick, and the remains of the smithy.

4 South of Wheal Metal are the extensive workings of Great Wheal Fortune tin and copper mine at 189/628285. It stopped working in 1867 and now all that remain are the farm that was once the manager's house, embankments that once carried tramroads, and wheel-pits and shafts now covered with wild red-berried cotoneasters.

BUDE

For details of the Bude canal see pages 130-2.

The gasworks (174/210055) was the last of twenty-six established throughout Cornwall over a very long period to produce gas for a Cornish town. It closed in May 1970.

The Falcon Inn is the oldest coaching house in North Cornwall, and was once the headquarters of coaches running between Bideford, Bude and Newquay. A former landlord, a Mr Brendon, operated a coach service as late as 1919, making this the last outpost of coaching in Cornwall. One of the Falcon's coaches, preserved in the inn, ran to the railway station until the 1920s.

CALLINGTON

One mile NNW at 186/355708, the remains of the once prosperous Redmoor lead mine. Its main shaft was 540ft deep in 1843 and it worked for periods up to 1894. During the forty years 1843–83, its lead ore raised realised £120,000, and the main engine house is recommended for preservation by the Cornish Engines Preservation Society.

Half a mile north of Redmoor at 186/358720 are the massive burrows and three engine houses of the Holmbush Mine also recommended by the society. This mine was working in the seventeenth century and in the mid-1900s was worked to a depth of over 1,000ft below adit level. The engine houses accommodated 50in, 39in and 18in engines in the late 1830s. It raised both lead and copper ore.

At Kelly Bray (186/360715) are the remains of Callington station on the PD & SWJ railway, 1872–1966.

CALSTOCK–GUNNISLAKE 'CIRCUIT'

One of the most fascinating areas in Cornwall for variety of industrial archaeology and spectacular scenery, this is contained within a rectangle, the grid references of the four corners being 186/373740, 187/450740, 187/450670 and 186/373670, see *Industrial Archaeology of the Tamar Valley* by Frank Booker for the full story.

Start the 'circuit' at 186/375723 on highway B3257 east of Kelly Bray. Here are the waste tips of Kithill Granite Quarry and the incline down which thousands of tons of silver-grey granite were trammed to the railway siding between Luckett and Callington. At Monkscross, on the road into Luckett village, see on the right the old station mistress' house of 1906, a lonely railway station 700ft above sea level. The trains last ran in 1966. Nearby, the chimney of a long arsenic flue from the mine variously called Wheal Martha, New Great Consols, Duchy Great Consols and other names. The village has remains of this mine in the valley floor with several engine houses, whilst on the hillside to the south, there are extensive remains at 186/386737 of its most recent working in 1947–54.

Return from Luckett to Monkscross, then via B3257 to the Chils-worthy turn, noting the adjoining engine house of East Kithill tin mine, working in 1909. The scant remains of the kilns of the Phoenix Vitrified Paving & Firebrick Works are at 186/395715; and at 187/400717 the more extensive remains of a brick and terra cotta works operating as late as 1935 as the Tamar Brickworks & Potteries Ltd, previously Tamar Firebrick & Clay Company. There are remains of a great circular kiln 120ft diameter divided into sixteen chambers, and 5ft wide flue which led to a stack 150ft high demolished thirty-five years ago. These works were established in 1873, and could produce 80,000 firebricks a week. Half a mile south-east near the 800ft summit of Hingston Down stands a tall chimney stack on the west side of the road. Seventy years ago, it was connected with three circular 'beehive' kilns, the operational works of yet another brick company, the Cal-stock Firebrick Company. Two of these kilns stood until 1969, but were sold for their value as rubble for hardcore and then demol-ished.

On the top of Hingston Down, see the remains of Hingston Down Consols Mine, already 800ft deep in the 1860s, and then employing 225. It produced a variety of metals—copper, tin, wolfram and arsenic—and was last worked in the mid-1920s. The Cornish Engines Preservation Society recommend preservation of the main engine house at Bailey's Shaft, a fine stone building with dark red-brick dressings, its windows still with their early Victorian 'Gothic' iron glazing-bars which may date it to the start of the mine in 1843, although there are iron ties, their flanges bearing the legend 'Tavi-stock Iron Works 1882'. Its shallow pitched and slated roof is not readily visible as there is a parapet wall and gutter, an unusual feature for an engine house but undoubtedly so built to give some wind protection to the slating on this high windswept site.

At 187/420718 are the Greenhill Arsenic Works of the Cornwall Chemical Company and, associated with them, Gunnislake Clitters Mine on the Tamar bank. An extensive complex of mining runs down the hillside to 187/424723 where there was once a tramway incline rising several hundred feet to the main railway line close by Chilsworthy station. Mining here went on to the 1920s, and 1,000ft due south of the old railway station is an immense chimney stack dated 1894 at the top of the long arsenic flue, its stone base about 30ft diameter. The buildings to the south-east were the arsenic works established in 1875 to treat ores from all over the district and incorporating a large cooperage for 500 barrels. Nearby to the north-west is Hill Westlake & Co's well-preserved brickworks operating in the 1930s but now disused, and at 187/425711, the site of the Sandhill firebrick works, operated by B. Johns & Company in 1860.

At Dimson is another huge kiln established by the Dimson Fire Clay Company, indicated on the 6in map as 'Plymouth Works', later on the Plymouth Fireclay Company with a 500yd long spur from the East Cornwall Minerals Railway into the brickworks. All of these brick, fireclay and terra cotta manufactories, Calstock, Phoenix, Tamar, Plymouth, Sandhill and the earliest Bealeswood (Bailswood on the 6in map) on the Tamar bank near Gunnislake Weir, were part of a great industry that produced enormous quantities of building bricks, fireclay linings for boilers, gas retorts and glazed terra cotta over a period of about eighty years between 1855 and 1935.

At 187/432722 is the magnificent late-medieval road bridge (c 1500–20), 182ft long of six arches which Pevsner claims is the 'best of all the Cornish granite bridges'. Leland states that this bridge was begun by Sir Perse Edgcumbe (d 1539). A little below the bridge on the west bank is the mouth of the drainage adit of old Gunnislake copper mine and 150yd further on, alongside the river-bank footpath, are remains of substantial lime kilns.

At 187/435715 is the Gunnislake gasholder, all that remains of the former gasworks opened by the Callington & Gunnislake Gas Company in 1872 and which was supplied with coal by barges until about 1914. About 800ft south and running parallel to the main river for nearly 500yd is the old Tamar Canal cut during the first decade of the nineteenth century to make navigation possible upstream of the adjoining weir. Nearby, see the ruins of the Tamar Paper Mill (Tamar Millboard Co 1852) which became the Tamar Bone-crushing Mill (for fertiliser) in the late 1870s but which was disused by 1905. At the south end of the canal is the lock and keeper's cottage.

At 187/430715 is Pearson's Quarry approached up a sloping track that suddenly devolves upon a lake almost surrounded by high sheer granite walls and with overhanging trees and foliage. Up to about sixty-five years ago, the quarry produced very close-grained porphyritic granite, not unlike that from Corennie in Scotland, and during its century of working from 1808, it was excavated down to about 130ft; it is now full of water. From this place, connected to the East Cornwall Minerals Railway, was taken huge quantities of stone for great forts around Plymouth, and for Blackfriars Bridge in 1869. The last owner, Pearson, employed 700 men in 1900.

About 500yd south is the Gunnislake station terminus of the branch railway line from Plymouth, the line running to buffer stops about 400yd north-west. Little alteration has been made since it was opened in March 1908, but only one track now comes into the island platform and the goods sidings have gone. Nearby are the extensive remains of Drakewalls tin mine, which once carried the title 'the Dolcoath of East Cornwall'. Tin-ore sales 1853–95 realised a third of a million pounds, most of it between 1853 and 1870.

At Albaston (187/425700) there are old maltings with their characteristic 'oast' cap, on the south side of the road from the village to Calstock. They were part of the Albaston Brewery closed in the 1920s and operated at Albaston House by Thomas Bowhay (d 1944). In the 1880s the Bowhay family were described as brewers, maltsters and tanners.

The road to Calstock passes over 'Train-a-Bridge' (the derelict section of the ECMR) and at 187/425695 are the remains of the Incline Station of this railway. See the old engine-shed water-tower and coal wharf; the stationary engine pulled two waggons up an incline nearly 800yd long, opened in 1860, from Calstock Quay to the summit 300ft above. The station-master's house was recently sold by British Railways, although the incline ceased when the Plymouth, Devonport & South Western Junction Railway opened in 1908. To the north are the engine houses of East Calstock copper mine.

In Calstock churchyard are several finely lettered slate tombstones to miners, particularly that of the boy Isaac Sleep who was 'accidently killed by the crank of the water wheel in the Virtuous Lady Mine' in 1831, aged only fourteen. Just below the church on the 250ft contour is the railway to Gunnislake, running through the Harewood Cutting that involved the removal by the navvies of over 40,000 tons of rock and overburden.

At the southern end of the cutting, look down into the great bend of the river encompassing the 'Harewood' peninsula, with the precipitous wooded slopes of Maddacleave Wood on the Devon side. At 187/450695 are the burrows of the old and long disused Harewood Consols copper mine. About 700yd south-west are the impressive ruins of Okel Tor Works, an old mine reopened in 1850. See the ruin of the 51in pumping engine house. Between 1858 and 1887 it raised copper, tin and arsenic to the value of nearly £100,000. There are extensive remains of the arsenic plant.

Calstock is a delightful hillside village on the north bank of the Tamar, once the port for loading huge quantities of granite, bricks, mineral ores and other local products into ships and barges. Before the construction of the railway incline from the western end of the quay up to East Calstock Mine in 1860, twelve years prior to the opening of the East Cornwall Minerals Railway, the narrow roads of this village were thronged with horses and carts bringing stone and ore to the quays. At 187/437685 see the recreation ground that was once named Williams Quay, after the Cornish copper 'baron' John Williams of Scorrier. Huge piles of copper ore were stacked awaiting shipment, and even today local children talk of going to play on the 'coppee'.

The former firebrick works on the main road west of the railway station now makes chip-baskets, part of the fruit industry that has gone on in this valley for at least two centuries (see *Industrial Archaeology of the Tamar Valley* for details). The north bank of the Tamar was once busy with commercial quays, Williams', Vosper's, Steamboat and Kelly's and at the western end, close by the foot of the incline, was the principal granite quay. Close by are three huge lime kilns, the skew-arched bridge that carried the mineral railway up its incline and a little building with a half-hipped roof, now the property of Calstock Marine Services, that for nearly half a century was the railway 'office'.

The glory of Calstock is its great railway viaduct, completed early summer 1907: 1,000ft long it stands 117ft above the river and is built of 11,148 concrete blocks that were made on the Devon side by the contractor, J. C. Lang of Liskeard. Between 1908 and 1934, there was a curious wagon hoist built to raise and lower trucks between the station yard and the quay, coming up to viaduct level alongside the first arches on the Cornish side. The trucks ran across a short steel bridge running parallel with the viaduct and into the lift cage, dropping 110ft down to the quay.

The 11 miles of this line from St Budeaux to Gunnislake is a fine example of late nineteenth and early twentieth-century railway building and gives the traveller magnificent views of landscape, river scenery and, for the last 3 miles, a panorama of the Calstock–Gunnislake area. In these days, when tourism is all important, it should be given as much publicity as the narrow-gauge railways in Wales that are now so much on the tourist map that they draw tens of thousands of passengers every year. It must not be closed.

In the Danescombe valley at 187/419698 is the ruin of the long-disused Danescombe Paper Mill (approx 1788–1857). Near Harrowbarrow (187/403700) are the extensive remains of Coombe Arsenic Works, working up to the 1920s; and to the north of them, the Prince of Wales Mine, very old, but working fairly continuously from 1864 to 1914 raising copper, tin and arsenic worth over £126,000. The dumps were treated in the 1940s. One engine house is recommended for preservation by the Cornish Engines Preservation Society.

West of Coombe works, over a distance of 1½ miles, are a group of old silver mines that have given the name of 'silver valley' to this district: Wheal Fortune (187/400700); Wheal Brothers (186/391700); 800yd west Silver Valley Mine (186/383700); East Cornwall St Vincent (186/385695); adjoining it Wheal Langford and a half-mile further west yet another mine, Silverhill (186/375696). But Collins in *Observations on the West of England Mining Region* says of them 'they have at many different times yielded rich silver ores but never in such quantities as to be of economic importance'.

The stream that rises at Silverhill and flows into the Tamar over 4 miles to the east at Cotehele Quay powered a number of corn mills: Harrowbarrow (186/386695); Barret's 400yd south-east; Glamorgan Mill (187/403685) and Morden Mill on the Cotehele Estate (National Trust) at 187/415682, where the waterwheel exists and where provender milling went on until 1965.

From the summit of Kit Hill (1,094ft) reached by a private toll road, there is a tremendous panorama over East Cornwall and the fascinating Gunnislake–Calstock area below. Here was Kit Hill Great Consols Mine, whose square chimney-stack 85ft high is preserved by the Duchy of Cornwall as a monument to the enterprise of the miners, brickmakers and quarrymen who contributed so much to the industrial scene of this exciting district over many generations.

CAMBORNE

The visitor to this industrial lung of Cornwall—home of three of Cornwall's four tin mines, a world-famous engineering firm that manufactures mining equipment, and the county's Technical College, as well as the Camborne School of Mines—should first direct his attention to Holman's Museum opposite the Public Library and the statue of Richard Trevithick. Here will be found a vast range of engines and tools associated with mining: a vertical steam-engine of 1870; early drills; a model of Trevithick's steam pole-pressure engine erected at Wheal Prosper in 1811 and of his double-acting water-pressure engine erected at Wheal Druid in 1800; a carriage of 1809 that was used by the directors of the Poldice Tramway. But the most important piece of working machinery is the 1850 Rostowrack rotative beam-engine from West's Foundry at St Blazey (stroke 6ft, cylinder 22in and speed 22rpm) that worked in the clay pits until 1953.

The remains of mines exist in such profusion that only a few can be listed:

1 The engine house of Great Condurrow, 1,000ft NW of Condurrow Methodist Chapel at 189/662391.

2 The impressive mass of buildings, ore-stamps, dressing-floors, tramways and stacks of South Wheal Francis at Carnkie (189/680395).

3 The engine house (189/660385) of Grenville United, built for Goold's 80in, pumping from 1,900ft.

4 The remains of the burrows of Tincroft, roughly on the site of Carn Brea station at 189/670409.

5 The extensive burrows, shafts and stacks of Carn Brea mines, alongside the railway.

Three other items of interest should be mentioned: Bickford Smith's one-time fuse factory at Tuckingmill (189/660410) with its plaque to William Bickford (1831); Trevithick's cottage at Penponds (189/636389); and the Camborne Literary Institution (1829) in the main square of the town.

CARHARRACK

About 1 mile to the east of the village are the extensive burrows and workings of the Consolidated Mines with the ruined walls of engine houses and the base of the massive clock-tower. Through them runs the track of the Redruth–Chasewater Railway. In Carharrack itself (190/732415), and now used as farm outbuildings, were the storage sidings, the great yard and office buildings of the railway company.

CARTHEW

At 185/004555 is Wheal Martyn clay works, closed 1966. To the north-west up a long tree-lined drive is the old Martyn family mansion, Carthew House, commenced in 1797 after the purchase of the estate in 1791. This is perhaps the last small family clay works left in Cornwall where all the various hydraulic processes, Cornish lift pump, mica drags, settlement tanks and kiln tanks, dry and linhay, all within a small area, can be readily comprehended. Here is the last complete Cornish lift, flat-rod and 25ft waterwheel with its balance box. There is also a larger 35ft overshot wheel made by the Charlestown Foundry that until recent years drove a flat-rod over a distance of 660yd to the pump at the Wheal Martyn clay pit to the west. This works must not be destroyed for it is a fine example of early clay technology.

At 185/997555, ½ mile due west of Wheal Martyn, is the 30in Greensplat beam-engine, perhaps made as early as 1830, that stopped on 22 February 1959, the last Cornish engine to work in Cornwall. It is owned by Berk Ltd.

CHACEWATER

On the hill to the west are the remains of the once thriving Wheal Busy (190/740448), the Cornish mine where James Watt first introduced some of his most important improvements to the steam engine in the 1770s. This mine was already working in 1718 and was still in work 200 years later. At 190/735443 the engine house of Wheal Killifreth (c 1880s) is reckoned to be one of the best in Cornwall and stands with a number of others silhouetted against the sky as one comes down into Chacewater from Truro.

At 190/739448 is the engine house (1858) into which the great 85in Perran Foundry engine was installed in 1909–10. It existed in 1944 and was recommended for preservation but was broken up the following year (plate, p 35). Nearby is the old smithy with a cast-iron arch from Perran Foundry dated 1872 with the inscription 'Great Wheal Busy Mines' and the remains of the arsenic calciner and its stack.

Between 1725 and 1815, Chacewater was particularly associated with the Shropshire family of engineers, the Hornblowers, who lived at nearby Salem. Jonathan Carter Hornblower (d 1815) is buried at St Gluvias churchyard, Penryn.

CHAPEL PORTH

At 189/701493 in Chapel Coombe, a set of old Cornish stamps recovered from a site at St Agnes has been re-erected through the energy of the Trevithick Society, complete with waterwheel, wheel pit and leat.

CHARLESTOWN

The harbour (185/039518) was excavated 1792–8 for Charles Rashleigh of Menabilly to the plans of John Smeaton, to ship china clay and copper ore from Pembroke, East Crinnis and other mines. It is still used for the shipment of china clay. John Lovering's tunnel and underground railway that he built for discharging his clay from Carclaze in 1908 can clearly be seen.

The foundry (185/038519) was started in 1827 and re-equipped in 1935 by English Clays Lovering Pochin & Co Ltd for their engineering maintenance work. Still working is the 30ft overshot waterwheel of 1852 that provided the power for the forge-hammers. Other items of interest are: a face-wheel; the original boiler house and chimney stack; cast-iron fluted columns for supporting the roof; beams of thick Cornish timbers that were standard size for mine pump-rods; and the house of the caretaker.

COVERACK

A small fishing harbour (190/783182) built of dark hornblende/ serpentine stone and bearing a stone inscribed 'T Ellis 1724'.

CROWAN

At 189/645342 is Crowan Mill, an ancient water-powered mill that ground corn up to 1946 and then became a well-known pottery. After the pottery closed, the mill was used for textile weaving and the wheel and machinery were 'in order' in sale particulars of April 1970. Overshot wheel made by J. Harvey of Helston.

DELABOLE

See full description in Chapter Eight, pages 161–7.

DEVORAN

At 190/794394 was the terminus of the Redruth–Chasewater Railway built to serve the copper mines at Gwennap in 1824. A 1 mile extension was laid to Point (190/810385) and, though no trace of it exists there now, its course can be followed along the road by the side of Restronguet Creek to Devoran, taking in the ruins of the half-submerged engine house of Upper Carnon Mine near the mouth of Tallack's Creek (190/802338).

At Devoran itself there are many reminders of this once busy port which, on its wooden wharf, handled millions of tons of copper ore and Welsh coal: walls of warehouses, stables and ore-storage bins; a line of massive granite mooring-bollards; the shipping office, now a private house; the company's offices; a locomotive shed also now a private house; the workshops used now by local voluntary organisations; and two granite posts to which were once fitted the gates that controlled the railway where it crossed the road. One of the gates and the stone weigh-house are still visible.

Just outside Devoran and off the main Truro–Falmouth road is Basset's Foundry (190/789395) that specialised in general and marine work. Once burned out, it still retains some of its original walls and three impressive waterwheels, one undershot and two overshot. The foundry is still active under the direction of W. Visick & Sons, pump and well specialists and marine engineers.

EGLOSHAYLE

At 185/020725, Hingham watermill is still daily used by the miller Mr A. Beare. It has an unusual undershot paddle-wheel 20ft diameter all in timber except for the iron shaft and the two concentric iron drum rings to hold the paddles in place. It drives one pair of stones made of French granite and a grinder made by Harris of Wadebridge. One of the last two working mills in Cornwall. (Sometimes incorrectly referred to as Lemail Mill.)

ENYS

At 190/790365 probably the oldest working waterwheel in Cornwall, 14ft 4in diameter made by the millwright Rapson in Penryn in 1821 for pumping water to the mansion.

FALMOUTH

The golden age of Falmouth was the nineteenth century. It was a packet station 1688–1852; port of refuge; centre of pilchard fishing; general trading port; a leading centre for the building of schooners and, in our own time, an important repair port for oil tankers. Its Royal Cornwall Polytechnic in Church Street, founded in 1833, bears witness to its concern for education in early technology as well as the arts. The founder was Robert Were Fox (1789–1877) of G. C. Fox & Son, shipping agents, who moved from Fowey to Falmouth in 1762.

The Georgian Royal Hotel was first lit with gas in 1817, but the town's gasworks established c 1830 have gone, as have the two breweries, Carne's and the Anglo-Bavarian. Of particular interest, note the Customs House of the 1820s in the Greek Doric style. The old Falmouth Union Workhouse (190/788334), built in 1852 for 320 inmates, was sited well away from the town, a practice common all over the country. It is now Budock Hospital.

Near Pennance Point (190/805306) are the remains of an arsenic works in operation in the seventies.

FOWEY & POLRUAN

A port, which R. Pearse in *Ports and Harbours of Cornwall* says was 'once one of the principal seaports of the United Kingdom, at which many vessels were fitted out for the Crusades'. It was never of great importance for the fishing industry, and its industrial importance is only a century old.

The railway arrived in January 1869 along the west bank of the river from Lostwithiel, and that year the first cargo of china clay was loaded into the hold of the schooner *Rippling Wave* bound for Genoa. The Board of Trade sanctioned the building of new jetties that same year and the establishment of Harbour Commissioners, who first met on 1 September 1875.

The clay jetties are strung along the west bank from Caffamill Pill northwards for over half a mile, centred on 186/127525, and have an extensive network of railway sidings with turntables enabling freight wagons to load direct into ships. The china-clay trade increases yearly, 806,730 tons being exported during the year ending 31 March 1970. Two of the old timber jetties are now condemned—the archaeological remains of a century of the clay industry.

The original Cornwall Minerals Railway from Par, with its mile-long Pinnock Tunnel that came to Fowey in 1873–4 from the west, has recently been taken up and its track made into a private road for lorries bringing clay to the jetties. Much of the enterprise for constructing them goes to the former GWR, the deep-water berth (no 8) being started in 1912, completed in 1921, and officially opened on 27 September 1923 with the loading of the ss *Edern*. Four new piers were built in 1960 and all the docks leased by English China Clays from British Rail in 1968. The largest ship to berth can take 10,000 tons of clay: Par only accommodating ships carrying up to 1,500 tons. At the foot of Custom House Hill is the Custom House with its brightly painted Royal Arms.

Of the former industry of shipbuilding, when fine schooners were built here, nothing is left, but the old Slades Yard (186/125510) on the east bank at Polruan still carries on under the name of C. Toms & Son Ltd who build boats. A century ago there were many ships chandlers in the town and at Chester House, J. Bennett & Sons are still in business. On the Polruan side opposite Fowey Harbour Quay, is the Brazen Island shipyard and slipway owned by the Fowey Harbour Commissioners and, adjoining the fourteenth-century blockhouse at Polruan, are the rails used formerly for launching the big pilot cutter.

The only remains of the gasworks, the company having been incorporated in 1893, is a gas-holder near the decaying GWR station of 1895. The Fowey lighthouse is a red-painted iron structure of 1892 called 'Whitehouse', marking the western side of the Polruan ferry. On the Town Quay is an uncharacteristic red-brick Working Men's Institute of 1868; and a folly that used to be a windmill is at 186/119518.

GOLDSITHNEY

Gundry's Bank (189/543306) is now a private house. It was owned by John Gundry and his brothers, mine adventurers and smelters, who were made bankrupt in the depression of 1815–19 through heavy losses in Wheal Vor near Breage, and Wheal Prosper in Marazion.

Wheal Neptune (189/541299) survives only in its burrows, shafts, and the base of an engine house on the east side of the lane leading from the Helston road to Perranuthnoe.

Tregurtha Downs tin mine (189/539311) is outstanding for its magnificent engine house that was once occupied by one of the most celebrated of Cornish engines. It was brought to Tregurtha Downs in 1882, 1,200 spectators gathering to see the arrival of the bob, weighing 40 tons, pulled by forty-five horses. In 1903 the engine was purchased by South Crofty for Robinson's Shaft and can be seen today in situ from the road leading up from Pool crossroads on A30 (see also p 245).

o

GORRAN HAVEN

An ancient fishing harbour, its first small pier of fifteenth-century date, its trade in the eighteenth and early-nineteenth century dependent on merchandise brought to it by barges and lighters, transhipped at Fowey. The pier (190/015416) was rebuilt in the 1820s and again reconstructed in 1888.

GRAMPOUND

In this village, which in the eighteenth century returned two members to Westminster, were two tanyards. The Fal Valley Tannery is now used for other purposes, but the Manor Tanyard (190/936438), owned by J. Croggon & Son, is the last tanyard in Cornwall for the making of heavy leather and contains much of archaeological interest: the original lime pits; old machinery which was turned by flat-rods connected to a waterwheel; and the trench in which the flat-rods were laid.

GUNNISLAKE—see CALSTOCK–GUNNISLAKE 'CIRCUIT'

GWEEK

In the eighteenth century this was the port (190/707265) for tin from the mines in the Wendron district to the north. There are three substantial quays, one still used to bring in coal for distribution in the Lizard area. In the last century they were alive with small ships bound for North America with emigrants.

At the quay on the east bank is a large old warehouse used by the Western Counties Agricultural Co-operative for ship-borne trade over a period of eighty years until 1962. This farmers' co-operative was started in or about 1879 by, *inter alia*, members of the Lukey family, but succumbed to intense competition by other firms in the early 1960s. Their Gweek warehouse was used to store fertilisers, barley and maize brought in by sailing ketches. An example of hard work for little wages is remembered by Mr Samuel Moyle of Gweek who worked at the warehouse for half a century. In 1922, he and a fellow workmate carried on their backs 200 tons of fertiliser up from the hold of the German ketch *Eliza* in 2cwt sacks into this warehouse, for 6s (30p) a day.

HALSETOWN

An industrial 'planned' village 1½ miles south-west of St Ives, built in the 1830s by the enterprising Mr James Halse, solicitor, politician and mining adventurer, to house several hundreds of his workpeople. He was Tory member for St Ives Borough 1826–38 and the houses and cottages were laid out in wide-spaced rows each with a substantial garden, unlike the tightly packed industrial towns. This project represents Halse's design to secure the franchise for his employees under the property qualification of the Reform Act 1832, and so to further his return to Westminster!

In addition to the tin mine nearby, the settlement had a rope factory. This has been the St Ives Steam Laundry since about 1900.

HAYLE

For the details of this 'new town' developed around two great foundries after 1780, see Chapter Five. The remains of Harvey's Foundry (1779–1903) is at Carnsew at 189/558372. Harvey's great quay lies opposite Penpol Terrace. The Market House (1839) is now Lloyds Bank. Close by the level crossing is the swing bridge, opened 1877, that is still used by freight trains using the Hayle Wharves Branch of British Rail that connects the main line with the Octel works adjoining the power station at the western end of Hayle Towans. Harvey's made this bridge for the GWR.

At Copperhouse (189/568380) are the metal-perforating works of J. & F. Pool Ltd (established 1848), their no 3 works in a granite building bearing the date '1839' adjoining the A30. On the opposite side of that road is the original Copperhouse Canal Dock, its walls built of copper-slag blocks. Close by is the red-brick chimney stack and auxiliary engine house formerly part of the Copperhouse Tide Mill (provender).

On the north side of Copperhouse Pool at 189/562381 near Phillack Churchtown, is Riviere House, now a youth hostel, built in 1791 by John Edwards of Ludgvan, manager and principal partner of the Cornish Copper Company. Alongside the north shore of the lake, now Coronation Walk, is the site of the track of the Hayle Railway and at 189/567383 perhaps the earliest (1835) steam-railway bridge in Cornwall, that carried the metals over the Phillack stream.

On Commercial Road is the Institute built (1894) at the instigation of the Cornish-born philanthropist W. Passmore Edwards—one of many which he financed in Cornwall. The architect was Silvanus Trevail of Truro.

At 189/575395 on Upton Towans are the remains of the site of the National Explosives Company's dynamite works opened in 1889.

HELFORD RIVER

From its bridgehead at Gweek to its entry into Falmouth Bay south of Toll Point Mawnan, the channel has been used for commercial navigation for perhaps twenty centuries. Smacks, ketches and schooners sailed or were towed up to remote quays. Today each year still sees the passage of six or more small motor ships bringing mainly a cargo of coal up to the old Gweek Company's quay on the west side of Gweek harbour. The channel swings from side to side of the wooded estuary and only ships drawing no more than 10ft of water can reach Gweek.

On the south bank, there are several places formerly used for loading and unloading cargoes, some of them associated with country mansions who at one time depended on a ship-load of coal in the early autumn for their winter warmth. Treath Harbour is at 190/ 763263; Frenchman's Creek had two quays at 190/748255; the mansion called 'Tremayne' had its own quay at 190/735260; and for commercial use there was Bishop's Quay at 190/722255. On the north bank, Merthen Quay (190/730260) was the highest point reached by the big Norwegian timber boats bringing in mining timber in the eighteenth and nineteenth centuries. Scott's Quay (190/738278) on the long Constantine Creek owed its existence to the one-time flourishing stone trade: there were no less than eight granite-quarrying firms operating in Constantine in 1935. There are two more quays at Port Navas (190/755277), the headquarters of the Duchy of Cornwall oyster fishery. Helford itself was once so busy a port that it supported a custom house.

HELSTON

This market town today shows few traces of its important connection with mining. That it was once a centre for the coining of tin is remembered now only by the name of its main thoroughfare, Coinagehall Street. The extent of its mining, agricultural, marine and fishing activities, however, can be gauged from the fine Folk Museum in the old Butter Market near the Town Hall. The former Meneage Union Workhouse of 1855 is now a hospital. There is a mill at 189/654276, and water-powered mills operated at Lower Town (189/659292) until the end of 1969.

HERODSFOOT

At 186/205608 see the remains of the East Cornwall Gunpowder Company's works, developed in the bottom of a deep and secluded valley.

At 186/212599 are the remains of Herodsfoot lead mine which sold nearly 20,000 tons of lead ore, much of it rich in silver between 1848 and 1884. In 1870, its workings were 1,000ft deep and provided employment for 150. It had two 50in engines in the charge of the celebrated Cornish engineer, Matthew Loam.

INDIAN QUEENS

Between 185/915598 and 189/924601 is the Toldish Tunnel of Joseph Treffry's first railway line that ran from Gullies Wharf near St Dennis to his new port at Newquay. The contract to build this tunnel was let in August 1840 and it was abandoned when the new GWR line from St Blazey to Newquay was opened in 1876. Note on the summit of the tunnel the derelict Indian Queens Colour Works (known locally as the 'paint mine') working an ochre deposit.

LAMORNA

At 189/447246 are two mills with derelict wheels, one made by Isaac Willey of Helston in 1907.

In Lamorna Cove itself, at 189/450240, is an unusual kiln built into the harbour wall. This produced lime that was used to act as a sealer between the granite blocks that were used for building the quay. The latter was erected 1853–4 to take away stone from the quarry on the north side of the cove.

At 189/442245 is the water-powered Clapper Mill.

LANIVET

At Lamorick (186/135643) is a set of 16 head ore-stamps, water-powered, fully operational in the 1930s, and last used as late as 1953. Part of Wheal Prosper & Michell, a very ancient open working, is at 186/030642.

LAUNCESTON

A town often called the 'capital of Cornwall' and indeed it was the county town until 1837 when the assizes were re-established in Bodmin. It is primarily an agricultural town and was a centre for serge production and the leather trade. The Launcestonian Richard Robbins (d 1910) wrote in 1899 that the Flemings established a tucking mill in the fifteenth century at Newport, a separate borough to the north of the town, and his son Sir Alfred Robbins stated in 1888 that this cloth factory was at Town Mills. These mills, water-powered, continued in production until about 1968 for corn.

The Robbins manuscript lists eight tanners operating in the nineteenth century and at St Thomas' Bridge the old Kenzey Vale tannery is still the premises of Hender & Sons Ltd, leather factors.

An old-established foundry, iron and brass, existed at St Thomas and was owned by William Langdon.

The Mechanics' Institute was founded in 1847 at the Central Subscription Room which still survives as the banqueting room of the White Hart Hotel in the main square.

The Launceston Gas Works was established as early as 1834 by Messrs Waygood & Porter of Beaminster, afterwards taken over by Henderson & Browning. Gasmaking has ceased as in all other towns in Cornwall but a gas-holder remains (189/329851).

There is a survival of the ancient craft of ropemaking in the town at Maunder & Sons Ltd, Rope Makers, 3 Race Hill, with the fourth generation still in the firm. Mr Richard Maunder who died in 1970 was proud of the fact that he had taught his sons to spin rope.

Launceston has completely lost its railways. The old GWR station of 1865 at 189/330850 remains, but little remains of the LSWR station of 1886 close by.

To the south-east of the town at Page's Cross (189/335838) is St Mary's Hospital built in 1838 as the Launceston Union Workhouse for 212 inmates.

LEEDSTOWN
East of the village along the road that leads to Crenver Grove (189/636339) are the burrows of Crenver and Wheal Abraham. In the woods near Godolphin Hall, at 189/599324, can be located the Godolphin Mine, where copper was worked before the seventeenth century.

LELANT
At 189/541365, by an old mill, is an overshot waterwheel driving a pump to supply water to the former mansion of Trevethow ½ mile to the north-west. This wheel, originally established in the nineteenth century, used to pump water to the reservoir supplying the village. It now pumps water used by the photographic company operating from Trevethow.

At 189/552375 is the old quay where the original fourteenth-century seaport was before St Ives came into being, and from whence the old Cornish firm of Bickford Smith, afterwards part of ICI, shipped explosives until very recent times.

LERRYN

At 186/140570 is the head of Lerryn creek and the remains of an isolated trading place situated at 'an innermost recess of a Cornish creek'. Here are two large kilns which used schooner-brought lime from Oreston quarries at Plymouth and, nearby, a simple and beautiful fifteenth-century bridge without parapets. Lerryn ceased to have any commercial river traffic after 1939.

LINKINHORNE—see ST CLEER & LINKINHORNE

LIZARD (THE)

The most southerly village in Britain, latitude 49° 58'. Still to be seen are small workshops where 'tourist ware' is made of the local serpentine; a trade that is still active after 150 years. The stone is quarried from small local pits. At 189/675145 is 'Soaprock' where steatite (soapstone) was mined in the eighteenth and nineteenth centuries and used as a detergent and in porcelain manufacture. At 189/705115 is the Lizard lighthouse (1752).

LOOE

On both banks of the Looe River are the quays that served as a port for the mining centre of Liskeard as far back as the middle of the thirteenth century; but it was the great mining activity in the hills north of Liskeard that brought about the extensive port development in the second quarter of the nineteenth century. The canal to Liskeard was opened in August 1827 and the new railway, bringing down copper ore and granite, was opened to the Moorswater (Liskeard) terminus of the canal in 1844 and then to Looe in December 1860. There is an interesting port warehouse (c 1850) at 185/255533.

From Looe was exported thousands of tons of granite used for the construction of forts and docks at Plymouth, Portsmouth and Spithead; the great breakwaters at Alderney, Dover and Plymouth; and the Thames Embankment in London.

Visit also the Cornish Museum at Lower Street, East Looe—a fascinating collection—particularly for the local items concerned with mining, fishing, early travel and illumination. The museum is housed in an old fish-cellar and it contains an old fish press, pilchard-oil pit and open hearth for smoking.

LOSTWITHIEL

The medieval 'capital' of Cornwall's tin industry and the place of the Stannary Parliament. The coinage hall still exists, much restored and called the Old Duchy Palace. As a port, it was important in medieval times but as in other localities, eg Pentewan, mining waste deposited in the river impeded the navigation which then passed to Fowey. Barge traffic between Fowey and Lostwithiel ceased about 1900.

The large and now disused carriage and wagon-works building of the Cornwall Railway (1858–9) is west of the railway station, itself an interesting industrial relic at 186/105597. See also the fifteenth-century bridge across the river adjoining the station.

LUDGVAN

At 189/480355 on Trenowin Downs is a very old china-clay works still operated for sand, that was restarted by W. K. Baker in 1868. (Borlase mentioned it in 1758.) The clay was formerly shipped from Penzance Docks to the Mersey and thence by canal to the Potteries.

LUXULYAN

At 186/055572 is the earliest great viaduct/aqueduct in Cornwall, designed by James Palmer and constructed 1839–42 at a cost of £7,000 by Joseph Treffry of Place House, Fowey, to carry his new railway from Par to Newquay.

MABE

At Carnsew (190/760345) are some of the once important sixty granite quarries of the Freeman & McLeod 'empire', established about 1848 by John Freeman and his two sons, that produced stone for great engineering works and lighthouses. There are other remains of this extensive industry at Spargo (190/750330) and at Long Downs (190/740345). One of the few quarries still to work is at Trolvis nearby. Freemans once employed 1,500 men.

MAKER

At Empacombe at 187/445529 there is the 25ft high tower of the old windmill, one of the six remaining in Cornwall.

MARAZION

At 189/528317 can be seen the shafts and mounds and excavations that were once Wheal Gwallon; and at 189/534318 the remains of the counthouse of Wheal Prosper. Gwallon was an old mine that was reopened for tin in 1817 by a group of adventurers that included six of the Gundry family. Water power was used by a system of leats that can still be traced from the stream that ran by Truthall Mill. In the depression of the 1840s all the machinery was sold and the mine completely abandoned, except for some reworking during the boom of 1906. Wheal Prosper was worked for tin and copper in the eighteenth century, and John Gundry invested heavily in it. In 1804 it had lost no less than £32,000. There were subsequent reworkings, and it was active again in the 1860s under the title of Prosper United.

In 1873 Marazion was importing timber, coal and iron and perhaps the only relic of this today is the capstan on the harbour wall on St Michael's Mount (189/514303).

Towards the east of the town on Turnpike Road is a tollhouse and close by a granite stone in which the spike turned. A dwelling-house near a garage (once a drill-hall) was formerly a blacksmith's shop. At the western end of the town over the marshes at 189/514312 is an old packhorse bridge and, close by, the Turnpike Trust Bridge of 1837.

At 189/506318 are some clay pits that gave the raw material for a small but flourishing Newtown brickworks (see page 198).

MARHAMCHURCH

At 174/220037 are the remains of the inclined plane, the first one on the Bude Canal where a 50ft waterwheel hauled tub-boats up a distance of 836ft and a vertical lift of 120ft.

At Helebridge (174/215037) are the remains of the canal wharf, the road bridge over the canal of the 1820s and the LSWR bridge of 1897 over the canal.

MENHENIOT

At 186/289635 is the old engine house of Wheal Trelawney, a lead and arsenic mine which worked throughout the 1840–90 period and again in 1900–2. At 186/292611 is the railway viaduct called Coldrennick where the steel-girder bridge of 1933 is still carried on the original Brunel piers of 1854–5 built for the Cornwall Railway.

MORWENSTOW

At Coombe (174/208118) is the old watermill, its machinery still in position, now Landmark Trust property.

MULLION

At Porth Mellyn (189/665179) is Mullion Harbour 1895, with its pier, recorded in 1935 as a place of call 'by pleasure steamers from Penzance in the summer months'. Here was an important water-powered mill hence the name Porth-Mellyn, the Cornish for Mill-Harbour. This was once an important pilchard-fishing centre.

MYLOR

At Restronguet (190/815365) and Enys (190/792364) are the remains of horse and oxen-driven corn mills, relics of the agricultural improvements of the mid-nineteenth century as particularly exhibited at the Great Exhibition of 1851. At 190/821353 and adjoining the parish church on the south bank of Mylor Creek, are the remains of a naval dockyard established in the eighteenth century.

NANCEGOLLAN

At 189/648333 is a fine old engine house of the Polcrebo Mine on Polcrebo Downs, a tin mine working in the 1890s, but of very ancient origin.

NANCLEDRA

At 189/500355 is a set of eight tin stamps driven by an 18ft × 29in waterwheel made by E. T. Sara of Camborne. They were working as late as 1945–50.

NEWBRIDGE

Roskennals watermill (189/431310) was the last mill for grinding corn to work in south-west Cornwall, driven by an overshot wheel, 13ft diameter, with a pair of 50in granite stones. Closed September 1970.

NEWLYN EAST

Between the village and the A30 road, at 185/838555, lie the remains—burrows, old dressing-floors and the counthouse—of Cornwall's most famous lead mine, East Wheal Rose. The massive engine house, heavily tied, owing to the use of freestone, was built to contain the enormous 100in engine of Michael Loam and dates to the final and disastrous reworking of the mine in the 1880s. The engine was mounted unusually high owing to the danger of flooding, a lesson learnt from the calamity of 1846, when a cloudburst destroyed the mine workings and caused the deaths of thirty-six men.

To the south-west are two other buildings of interest: the powder-house of Shepherds United Mine; and Shepherds, the house built in

1819 for John Giddy, the manager of Old Wheal Rose and the superintendent of the smelting house.

NEWLYN WEST

The harbour installations were originally designed for the once famed and large fleet of pilchard boats. Many houses, as well as the local ice-factory, still indicate the importance of the industry when the pilchard was the main diet of the Cornish. There are examples of fish cellars and long rooms for the making and drying of nets, while several houses possess doors some 6in wider than usual to permit easy exit and entrance of fish barrels.

Penlee Quarry (189/468278) has the most westerly railway in England, a 2ft narrow-gauge, for discharging stone into waiting ships at the harbour. Its original steam locomotive can be seen in the quarry, which has an interesting connection with mining, for within its boundary at 189/470279 is the site of the West Tolvadden Mine. Worked for copper between 1858 and 1863, two of its levels ran under the sea and one of these recently became exposed in the quarry itself.

At 189/455294 is a group of buildings that once comprised Trereife smelting house. Originally established before 1732 and known locally as Stable Hobba, it was associated with John Batten & Son of Penzance and later, in 1872, with T. W. Field, a banker and owner of several arsenic factories in West Cornwall. In the depression of the 1890s it became a storage depot for copper ore from Levant Mine, while awaiting shipment from Penzance, and is now occupied by a firm making fish manures.

NEWQUAY

On the south side of Lehenver Lane, now known as Mount Wise, is the site of the Newquay silver and lead mine. The main shaft was situated on the 200ft contour, near the north-east corner of the present recreation ground and was served by an adit that still discharges its water on Towan Beach. It ceased working in 1845 when the counthouse was used as a school for navigation, and is now a store operated by the South Western Electricity Board (185/811613).

The harbour was built in 1833 by Richard Lomax at a cost of £10,000 for the purpose of shipping out china clay from the Hensbarrow district (p 37). It was acquired in 1838 by J. T. Treffry of Fowey who by 1849 had linked Newquay and Par with a railway. This involved building an inclined tunnel from the harbour, now an aquarium, and parts of the old railway cutting are still visible between the railway station and the harbour. His timber viaduct over the Trenance valley was replaced by the present graceful one of stone in 1938–9 and the railway double-tracked.

At Trevemper (185/823600) is a group of interesting warehouses built originally for housing corn and manures prior to distribution to local farms. Later they were used for a coal siding, the coal being brought in on a loop of the Newquay–Chacewater line. There are fish cellars on Town Road in Newquay and some near the Atlantic Hotel.

Charles Hadfield in his *The Canals of South West England* has indicated the importance of the St Columb Canal for he remarks: 'We may date the beginning of the canal age in the south at 1773 when the blind John Edyvean obtained his act to build the St Columb Canal high on the cliff at Trenance Point.' The act of parliament empowered him to construct bridges, tunnels, aqueducts, sluices, weirs, 'pens', water-tanks, reservoirs, drains, wharves, quays, weighbeams and 'engines'. The conveyance of shelly sand from the beaches for manure seems to have been the most important reason for the canal.

Two sections were built, one from the sea at Trenance Point to Whitewater and the other from Lusty Glaze in St Columb Porth inland, both following the 180ft and the 100ft contours where land was cheap but involving the engineers in construction problems of some difficulty. Parts of it were never finished, G. B. Worgan in his

General View of the Agriculture of Cornwall of 1811 does not mention it, and in 1824 it was said that few traces of it remained. The beginning of the Lusty Glaze section can be clearly seen in a sharp cut in the cliff up which the tubs containing sand were hoisted. The Trenance–Whitewater section has recently been mapped by some of the pupils of Treviglas Modern School, Newquay.

Other remains of interest near Newquay are: a lime-kiln on a small quay at Penpoll Creek on the Crantock (south) side of the Gannel (185/798608); a horse-whim house for grinding corn in the village of Crantock (185/791604); a corn mill, now a private dwelling-house called Sunset Strip at Rejerrah (185/803565); also at Rejerrah the engine house of Wheal Mexico (185/797563), a silver-lead mine; a mill at Treago West Pentire (185/781601); a lead smelter on the Crantock side of the Gannel between Penpoll Point and the beach road from Crantock (185/794608); and a corn mill at Kestle Mill (185/851593).

PADSTOW

This Atlantic terminus of the LSWR was opened in March 1899 but the track along the south side of the Camel Estuary was taken up in March 1967, leaving but few remains of this railway enterprise. See at 185/925741 the iron railway viaduct of 1898 across Little Petherick Creek that may become a bridge for a new bridle way from Wadebridge. The quays and harbour are full of interest and the ancient craft of boat-building continues. See in particular the north quay warehouse.

At 185/897750 is the base of a windmill, its top surmounted by a water tank and with a pointed 'Gothic' window on its north face.

At 185/914780 the remains of Stepper Point Elvan Quarries and pier just north of Hawker's Cove, and at 185/862760, Cataclews Point, where the famous elvan 'catacleuse' stone was quarried, mentioned in Carew's *Survey* of 1602. At 185/851766 is the Trevose Head Lighthouse of 1847.

PAR

One of the most important ports in Cornwall today, its harbour was artificially created by Treffry (p 106).

Parts of the canal from Par to Pontsmill are discernible: one lock minus gates near the gasworks on the harbour; the bridge that carried the canal over the Par River; the canal itself from the railway crossing at 185/075535 up to the St Blazey railway crossing at 185/071553; and the canal basin at Pont's Mill at 185/073563 together with the loading wharf for the granite and copper ore.

For Treffry's mineral railway up the Luxulyan valley see page 39.

There are two other items of unusual interest in the district:

1   William West's Foundry founded in 1847 at St Blazey (186/ 068549), the original wooden gates still intact.
2   The remains of the foundations of the enormous 237ft stack of the silver-lead smelting works, which stood in the harbour about 100ft inland from the main road.

PENDEEN

At Pendeen Cove, sometimes known as Boat Cove, are remains of fish cellars and a capstan, indications that some of the miners were also fishermen. The major mine in the area was Wheal Hearle, whose two engine houses still survive on the exposed moor close to the Pendeen–Penzance road at 189/399335. The counthouse is nearer the coast at 189/384356.

The lighthouse and its shore station at 189/379360 were completed in 1900.

PENRYN

So much of the old industries have gone—granite dressing from over fifty quarries in the hinterland which was carried on in extensive yards on the southern shore of the Penryn River where Harvey's yard now lies; flour and paper mills; and engineering works casting the stamps for ore-dressing. The cluster of old warehouses and timber yards adjoining the town bridge at the head of the river (190/789342) include a typical warehouse building of the early nineteenth century that was a manure factory—the West of England Bone & Manure Co—for a long period. Boat-building still continues, carrying on a tradition that once produced fine schooners for the Newfoundland run. The original Cornwall Railway station building of 1862–3 stands apart, 8oft north-east of the new station built in 1923. Also here is the goods shed of 1862 in local stone with large queen-post roof truss. See also the last of the great stone viaducts to be rebuilt on this line, Collegewood (190/781342), constructed in 1933–4, with the piers of Brunel's 1862 bridge alongside. Nicholas Sara's foundry here built a broad gauge engine for the South Devon Railway in 1868, still to be seen on the down platform at Newton Abbot station.

PENTEWAN

At 185/019473 was the terminus of the railway of 1829 that began on West Hill in St Austell at 185/010523. The harbour never overcame the problem of silting caused by the detritus of powdered quartz and mica brought down the river from the clay workings and is now completely derelict. Among the industrial remains to be seen are: the pier, on one stone of which are inscribed the Hawkins' arms, the date '1826', and the legend SIR C. H. BRT.; the basin, the lock gates, a clay shed; and the four reservoirs, now dried up and overgrown, that were constructed in the 1840s to provide flushing power to deal with the problem of silting. The last ship called in 1940.

At Pentewan nothing remains of the original railway, though its bed by the river is easily recognisable and can be followed now and again as a low embankment. At London Apprentice (190/008499) is a shed that was part of the coal yard and siding that served Polgooth. Beyond this point to St Austell the railroad is almost impossible to discern.

PENZANCE

While Penzance is not especially rich in strictly industrial remains, there are many buildings of interest and importance that are indicative

P

of its past industrial wealth: the rooms of the Royal Cornwall Geological Society (founded in 1814) in the Municipal Buildings with its unique mineral collection; the Penzance Library in the Morrab Gardens (founded in 1818) with its special collection of Cornish books; the Assembly Rooms, now the Union Hotel, in Chapel Street; and to its rear the remains of an eighteenth-century theatre. A house in Penlee Park is noteworthy for it contains the Borough Museum and its many items of interest associated with local industries: bank notes; coinage tokens; the wooden wind-bore of a mine pump; a carbon crucible for the assaying of tin, etc. Banking is represented by the old Devon & Cornwall Bank (1892) at 3 Market Place, in its basement ceiling are rails from the old GWR broad-gauge tracks, which were taken up that year.

Industrial installations of note are: the fine and extensive harbour, including the Albert Pier of 1853, and the floating dock built by the Penzance Corporation in 1884; and the many solid granite warehouses in Bread Street near the railway station, and on the sea-front, one of which was built to contain the first refrigeration plant. In 1840 Holman's Foundry was started to specialise in marine work (as it still does) and remains of two of the original furnaces can be detected at the rear of the gasworks. With its other foundry at St Just, established 1834 and demolished 1968, the firm also produced much of the general ironware in the town. Their dry dock was built in 1880.

Penzance's connection with mining begins with its being a coinage town and, though the hall has long disappeared, its site is perpetuated in Coinagehall Street, near the Barbican. More important was the Chyandour Smelting Works on the outskirts of the town at 189/479311, built by the Bolitho's on the site of a blowing house. Though the works have disappeared, the industrial complex is readily recognisable on the ground: workers' cottages; the blacksmith's shop; the entrance to the smelter (now a coal yard); Ponsandane, the great house of the Bolitho's, the stables with their clock tower, and the ornamental horse trough.

There were two tin mines within the immediate neighbourhood of Penzance: Wheal Wherry (189/468295) and the Mexico Mine (189/499313). Both of them ran beneath the waters of Mounts Bay. Wheal Wherry was first worked in 1790 from two shafts, but was destroyed during a storm in 1798 when an American ship collided with its rigging. It was reworked in 1835 with a 40in engine for pumping that was connected to the shaft by a complicated run of flat-rods. The Mexico Mine, also known as the Long Rock Mine, was roughly on the site now occupied by the Mexico Inn and was worked between 1819 and 1823 by one Henry Pascoe without success because a gale destroyed the fabric of the shaft.

Two other places of industrial interest in the immediate vicinity of Penzance are: the mead factory in Gulval in the premises of a granite flour mill; and the Union Workhouse at Madron (189/452323), a 'Gothic' building now partly in ruins, built in 1838 at a cost of £6,000 to house a permanent population of 400 paupers.

PERRANWELL

At 190/780398, see original Cornwall Railway station (1862–3) with its curious signal box perched high on a staging over the old siding into the goods bay and so giving the signalman a good view of trains in both directions on a curving stretch of line.

PERRAN WHARF

See Chapter Three, pages 47–8.

PERRANZABULOE

This parish abounds in old mine workings and between Penhale and Shepherds (185/757590 to 185/810540), a distance of 5 miles, are the various mines of the Great Perran iron lode. Penhale iron mine is nearest to the coast, and extending south-eastwards along the line of the lode are Halwyn, Mount, Treamble, Great Retallick, Duchy Peru and Deerpark Mines. They were worked mainly in the period 1860–90 and produced 200,000 tons of high-grade iron ore. During

World War II, Treamble and Mount were again worked, using the
Treamble branch of the GWR from Shepherds, now taken up.

POLBATHIC

This hamlet at 186/348569 lies at the head of a narrow creek that
runs into the St Germans or Lynher River at St Germans Quay. Here
there still exists the East Cornwall Iron Works founded by William
Brenton about 1850 and still trading under that name. Iron-foundry
work was carried on here until 1968, but a rare feature of this small
rural works is its hot-dip galvanising process. Its main trade over
four generations has been in agricultural machines, and at one time
its labour force was eighty-five men.

The buildings of an old watermill still exist adjacent to the garage
of A. W. Bringham. About fifty years ago a water turbine was installed
in the mill to generate electricity for the hamlet. Although this power
source ceased over forty years ago, during the survey for this book in
1970, there were discovered in a shop here and *still for sale*, a quantity
of 50V carbon-filament Crompton light bulbs in demand by the
villagers during the 1920s!

POLKERRIS

At 186/095521 on the eastern side of St Austell Bay, is the old
harbour of Polkerris with its slate pier of the 1730s. Here is the
extensive and impressive ruin of what is claimed to be the largest
fish cellar (pilchard-curing factory) in Cornwall and, close by, a large
lime kiln. Note the old cannons set into the pier for mooring
posts.

POLRUAN—see FOWEY & POLRUAN

PONSANOOTH

Between 190/745370 east of Stithians and 190/771380 is Kennal
Vale whose stream has provided water power for several industries
(see pp 201-3, Chapter Nine). Part of a huge waterwheel 11ft wide

is still extant that powered W. S. Williams & Co's paper mill a century ago. Ponsanooth Viaduct (190/762376), 140ft high, is the loftiest of the four stone viaducts on the Falmouth branch built by the GWR between 1927 and 1934.

PONT

At 186/145520 at the head of Pont Pill, a creek on the east side of Fowey Harbour, are a water-powered saw mill and lime kiln, now a National Trust property.

PONT'S MILL

At 186/072562 the complex of china-stone grinding mills was in operation until the mid-1960s, powered by water turbines fed by the leat across the Treffry Viaduct (pp 119–20). Here also is the head of the Treffry Canal from Par, opened 1847 and, nearby, at Carmears (186/166565) the inclined plane operated by waterwheel on the Treffry mineral tramway from Par to Newquay.

POOL

The area abounds in old mining remains but there are three items of exceptional interest:

At 189/675416 alongside the A30 trunk road is the East Pool whim, the last rotative beam winding-engine in Cornwall. It was made at the Holman Foundry in Camborne in 1887, first saved for posterity by the efforts of the Cornish Engines Preservation Society founded in 1935 and is now in the care of the National Trust.

At 189/679419, also owned by the National Trust, is the Harvey Foundry (Hayle) 90in beam pumping-engine at Taylor's Shaft of the old East Pool & Agar Mine. Made in 1892 by the Harvey Foundry, Hayle, it ceased work in September 1955.

At 189/669409, also owned by the National Trust but at the head of Robinson's Shaft within the surface buildings of South Crofty Mine, is the 80in beam engine made at the Copperhouse Foundry in 1854.

PORT GAVERNE—see PORT ISAAC

PORTHCURNO

At 189/383227 is the Engineering School of Cable & Wireless Ltd. Here the British end of the cable from Bombay came ashore in June 1870 and so was established the first long distance cable in the British Empire. The cable station was operated by the Eastern Telegraph Company 1872–1934, and closed in 1970.

PORTHLEVEN

The harbour (189/628258) was originally constructed between 1816 and 1818 but was never satisfactory until 1854 when the Harveys of Hayle leased it. They built the present breakwater and inner basins with flood gates and sluices on the pattern of their other harbour at Hayle, so facilitating ships to remain afloat whatever the state of the tide, and did not relinquish the lease until 1961.

Two miles west of Porthleven, on a striking position on the cliff edge, are the two granite engine houses of Wheal Trewavas (189/600265), abandoned in the 1850s when the sea broke into the workings. At 189/592272 above Rinsey Cove can be seen the finely proportioned engine house of Wheal Prosper, working for copper 1832–49 and now a National Trust property. Other mines of interest are: Wheal Saturn (189/628266), a lead mine whose site is marked by a single burrow in a field about 2,000ft south-west of Ventonvedna Farm; Antron Consols (189/628277) worked for copper in the 1850s, the sole remains of which is an adit that opens below the bridge near the road that leads to Porthleven; Wheal Penrose (189/634252) and Wheal Rose (189/638247). The latter were both silver-lead mines of great antiquity, perhaps dating back to Roman times, but they were certainly being worked in the 1580s by the Mines Royal.

PORTHOUSTOCK

At 190/808218 is the pier on the north side of the cove erected in

1895 by the St Keverne Stone Company for loading crushed stone direct into ships' holds (plate, p 89). It was used until December 1958. At 190/804202 is a pier of similar date still in use by a local stone company at Dean Point.

PORTHTOWAN

In the long-exhausted coppered canyon that leads to the sea are several engine houses of interest: Wheal Ellen (189/704469); Tywarnhayle (189/702472); United Hills (189/697474); and Wheal Lushington (189/692479) on the beach at Porthtowan, now converted into a dwelling-house. South Towan, immediately north of Tywarnhayle at the junction of the Redruth–Scorrier–Porthtowan road, is recommended for preservation by the Cornish Engines Preservation Society.

PORT ISAAC

At 185/995806 and 185/002810 respectively, Port Isaac and Port Gaverne were once a centre for export of slates from the quarries at Delabole and the surrounding district. They are still a centre for fishing. At 185/040789 see the old North Cornwall Railway station at Port Isaac Road now bereft of its railway. Built in 1893–4 of local stone it played its part in the social history of this lonely countryside until British Rail closed the line in 1966. It is representative of the other eight stations between Launceston and Wadebridge.

PORTREATH

At 189/655454, and one time known as Bassett's Cove, the harbour works as we now know them were started in 1760 by the Portreath Company, under a lease from Sir Francis Basset, for the import of coal and iron from South Wales and the export of copper ore to Swansea. Much later, this necessitated the building of two mineral lines, the Poldice Tramroad and the Hayle–Portreath Railway (pp 30 and 31).

PORTSCATHO

An old fishing quay (190/879352), of some interest perhaps for the fact that 'Covers Seining Co Ltd Seine Owners' was the only such concern listed in the last issue to be published of Kelly's *Cornwall Directory* 1935.

PORT WILLIAM

At 185/047864, at the south end of Trebarwith Strand, are the remnants of a place that was once the 'chief port for its slate quarries', the derelict remains of which are seen alongside the valley running inland to Trewarmett where there are extensive old quarries.

REDRUTH

In the general proliferation of mines and their remains, with which the landscape is smothered, the following may be noted:

1   The stack of Ped'n-an-Drea tin mine immediately behind the railway station. One of Cornwall's greatest tin mines, it was hardly ever more than a financial disaster and the stack of stepped rings remains as a permanent landmark to its losses. Originally 140ft high, its purpose was to accommodate the 70in engine of Woolf, but it was in use only until 1827 and afterwards was only a landmark, from the top of which, in 1832, barrels of tar were ignited to celebrate the passing of the Reform Bill.

2   The engine house and stack of Wheal Uny, about ⅓ mile SSE of St Uny church, Redruth.

3   The engine house of Old Cook's Kitchen, immediately north of the railway line and ¼ mile north of the village of Brea.

4   The engine house of Three Stacks Mine on the west side of Tolskithy valley (Illogan) and 1,800ft east of Broad Lane Methodist Chapel.

5   The engine house of Wheal Grambler, midway between Redruth and St Day and on the south of the road near Trefula.

Other buildings to be noted are:

1 The Tolgus Foundry at 189/692426. It has been in existence since 1860 and is still owned by the same firm, who still employ the original sources of power: a 30ft overshot waterwheel driving the fan for the main furnace that smelts the iron; and a 15ft waterwheel driving the machinery in the workshop by a complicated system of wheels and belts.

2 The Mining Exchange, built 1880 at Alma Place.

3 The home of William Murdoch, mining engineer and inventor of gas lighting in 1792, in Cross Street.

4 A continuous line of tin-streaming works on the left-hand side of the road to Portreath; and on the same road at Plain-an-Gwary the remains of the stack and buildings of the British & Foreign Safety Fuse Company, now being restored by Devenish Breweries.

5 At 189/690438, see the Tolgus Tin Company's works dating back over several centuries and operated by the Stewart family for more than 150 years up to 1968. Here is probably the only working set of Cornish stamps in the world; its drum came from the Pearce Foundry in Tavistock. The arsenic calciner, a rotating furnace used to burn arsenic from tin ore, is a Brunton type made about 1910 and was at one time at Polhigey Mine, Wendron. It was re-erected here in the early 1930s and was continuously in use for about fifteen years. These works now extract tin from three sources: waste left at old mines; beach sand from Gwithian; and ore received from 'tributers', ie miners working by themselves; and they are so interesting that over 30,000 visitors came to see them in 1970.

6 The chief offices of the South Western Electricity Board at Pool, formerly the depot of the Camborne–Redruth Tramways 1902–27, electricity being generated at Carn Brea power station until it shut down in 1913.

7 The Redruth Union Workhouse, now Barncoose Hospital, behind which are the remains of several associated buildings: the mortuary, a boot-repairing shed, pigsties, storehouses, a cook-house and a paved space where stones were broken by the paupers.

RELUBBAS

Three engine houses of interest are at: Tregembo Mine (189/572318); Tindene, 1 mile west of Godolphin Hill; and West Godolphin (189/582317) known locally as Wheal Junket. At 189/564312 may be seen some of the workings of the once very prosperous copper mine of Halamanning where, in the eighteenth century, power was provided by two Boulton & Watt engines.

ROSEWORTHY

At 189/616397, a famous hammer mill was established about 1790 and continued to make the special 'Cornish' shovel, as well as engine boilers and chains until 1939 when the plant was dismantled. The hammers were removed in 1941. Fortunately, there is a model of the mill at Holman's Museum in Camborne.

At 189/610401 are the remains of the English Arsenic Company's works at Newmill, established some time before 1873 and closed down during World War I. It made white powder, and red and lump arsenic.

Against the hillside are substantial remains of ovens, the lambreth or labyrinth of chambers used to condense the soot, which was swept out by hand labour, and the several flues that join one main underground flue that runs up the hillside for about 800ft to the foot of an immense chimney, about 100ft high. The sloping flue emerges from the ground at the foot of this stack, whose walls are 6ft thick at the granite base, merging into slate-killas and then a top section of red-brick. The chimney was sited on the south-western edge of the deep valley to assist in the problem of 'chemical fallout'.

RUTHERNBRIDGE

At 185/013668 is the 500 years-old road bridge of local blue stone and, close by, West Ruthern stamps, the only completely wooden stamps existing in Cornwall together with their 15ft waterwheel, used for bone crushing.

The railway navvies came in 1833 to construct a branch of the Bodmin & Wadebridge Railway, its trade concerned with coal, roadstone and ore from the local Mulberry Hill Mine at 185/020658. The last train ran in November 1933. Here there was a thatched cottage let by the LSWR to their 'female wharfinger'!

ST AGNES

In the neighbourhood of 190/710507 are three engine houses recommended for preservation by the Cornwall Engines Preservation Society: Wheal Coates (189/700501) on the cliffs north of Chapel Porth; Wheal Friendly (190/720512) ¼ mile due north of St Agnes church; and Blue Hills (190/728517) in Trevellas Coombe.

Other houses of distinction are: Wheal Charlotte (189/697492) in the valley above Chapel Porth; Wheal Kitty (190/726509) with its crenellated stack for a 65in engine built at the Perran Wharf Foundry; Goonlaze (190/725516) with remains of stamps and dressing-floors, for it was a giant producer of tin; and Polberro (190/715515) that gave such pure tin that it was conveyed directly to a smelter.

In the cliffs to the west of Trevaunance Cove (190/720517) are substantial remains of the cavernous excavations of Wheal Luna and the walls of storage bins. Under the supposed shelter of the cliffs a harbour was built and a platform erected above by means of which sailing vessels laboriously loaded ore and unloaded coal by horse-whims. The level of the platform can distinctly be seen but the harbour was finally destroyed by a storm in 1934, its stones still visible at low tide.

In the 1870s Trevenaunce Coombe was being used for all mining purposes with an arsenic works at the upper end and a progression of waterwheel stamps and tin dressing-floors all the way to the shore. All that now remain are overgrown leats, wheel-pits and some substantial walls bracing the western cliffs.

In St Agnes itself a building of considerable interest is the Mechanics' & Miners' Institute with a representative selection of photographs of this once-famous mining region.

ST ANTHONY-IN-ROSELAND

At 190/845312 is the Georgian lighthouse, the St Anthony light, built 1834-5.

ST AUSTELL

The commercial centre of the china-clay industry, and a town that was connected by a new railway (1829) to the port of Pentewan. No trace of the railway remains. Its northern terminus was at the foot of Western (now West) Hill adjacent to the foundry and gasworks and its sidings ran into these works so that wagons of coal could be brought straight from ships into the gasmaking plant, established about 1870.

Several old buildings of the foundry, shown on a map dated 1842, are still extant and used by Harvey & Co Ltd. Over one entrance is a cast-iron arch bearing the legend 'St Austle Foundry 1849'.

A tin smelter was recorded in the town in 1689, and there were 'three blowing houses' (smelters) in the 1820s. In Pond-dhu Road there was Lower Blowing House, which in 1933 was used as a corn mill worked by water-power and which had previous to this been a candle factory. When the building was demolished in June 1970, a large block of granite came to light containing two recesses used for pouring in molten tin to form ingots of metal. In Blowing House Lane, almost under the GWR curved granite Trenance Viaduct of 1898, there exists Higher Blowing House, a complex of tall buildings up to five storeys high, that became a water-powered corn mill and which are a good example of mill architecture, built partly of granite and partly of grey brick. Smelting had finished by 1880. The old St Austell Foundry is the site of the third smelter.

There is an old corn mill in Truro Road that was operating in the 1930s under H. G. Penwarden and is now a tyre store.

At 185/025548 is the huge open-cast clay working of Carclaze, but mined for tin, according to legend, as far back as the fifteenth century. In 1892 the pit was at least 18 acres in extent at the top and over 130ft deep. The changeover from tin to china-clay extraction occurred in 1870, and the working has been much extended.

The use of electric power in the clay industry brought about the establishment of an electricity works in the town in the 1880s, the first town so provided in Cornwall and a very early pioneer in Britain in urban electricity supply. The building still exists on a site 200ft west of the Market House, in the town centre.

The name of Walter Hicks is well known in St Austell. The family came from Luxulyan and Walter established a wine business in 1851 in a Georgian building opposite the parish church, now the 'Co-op'. Nine years later he started the brewing of beer at Tregonnissey House close by. This brewery continued in strength for forty years until the Hicks family established their brewery in Trevarthian Road in 1891 (p 192). Two Marshall & Paxman steam engines provided the power for this brewery but were scrapped in 1962.

To the north of the Bodmin Road car park, the extensive buildings still exist of the former St Austell Union Workhouse designed by Messrs Scott & Moffat, Architects, London, and built 1839, no longer used for the accommodation of 390 paupers.

At 185/055523 is an ornate castellated granite bridge (c 1850) which carried the Cornwall Railway line over the private road into Carlyon Bay and built at the request or perhaps insistence of the Carlyon family.

Finance for the mining and clay industry brought about the establishment of local banks throughout Cornwall during the nineteenth century and there were four such in St Austell. The premises of one of them, the St Austell branch of Shilson Coode & Co established in 1826 and lasting as such for almost a century until incorporated by the National Provincial in 1923, remains in the flamboyant red terra-cotta and red-brick building in High Cross designed by the Truro Architect, Silvanus Trevail, and dated 1898.

ST BREWARD

At 189/185752 is the Wenford Bridge terminus of the old Bodmin

& Wadebridge Railway, now the most northerly point of the railway system in Cornwall. Here, by quarry railway between 1834 and 1960, came tens of thousands of tons of fine dressed granite from the famous De Lank Quarries for destinations all over the world. These quarries (189/102753) are still in work after about 225 years (p 172).

ST BURYAN

At Alsia (189/395252) is a corn mill, with 13ft timber wheel of considerable age that was in continuous use until 1966. At Bottoms (189/395242) are the old buildings of a butter and cheese factory working as the Land's End Co-operative Dairy from 1890 to the mid-1930s, one of several local farmers' co-operatives in the Penwith area.

ST CLEER & LINKINHORNE

To the north, west and south-west of the 1,212ft summit of Caradon Hill, lie a cluster of old mining settlements, mines, quarries and the remains of the Liskeard & Caradon Railway. The furthest north of these settlements is Henwood (189/265735) with Minions, Darite and Tremar to the south. The stannary town was Liskeard.

Here were great copper mines like South Caradon and its associated ventures, and the Phoenix United Mine (186/266719) whose sales of tin and copper ores realised £1,317,000 between 1843 and 1899. Here was the famous Cheesewring Quarry (186/249725) owned by the Duchy of Cornwall and part of the 'Freeman & McLeod empire' in the 1930s.

The landscape for miles is liberally strewn with mine engine houses, John Allen's *History of Liskeard* lists fifty-nine engines in work 1853-4 varying in size from 16in to 80in at Phoenix; mine buildings; huge waste tips; and the silent quarries whose hard blue granite used to be trammed into Looe for shipment. The old Caradon Railway track wanders through this area, old bridges still extant, its northern extremity reaching out to the quarries at Kilmar Tor,

whence a proposal was made in 1882-4 to continue the line northwards and eastwards to join the LSWR then approaching Launceston
from Halwill Junction in Devon. See three engine houses of Wheal
Jenkin (186/265714), those of the Marke Valley Mine (186/278718),
of South Phoenix (186/263714) and those of South Caradon Mine on
the south-west slopes of Caradon Hill.

ST COLUMB MAJOR

See at Whitewater Farm (185/903656) the remains of the St
Columb Canal (for details see Newquay), and in the town itself at
185/914636 an elegant building designed in 1874 by the architect
William White in a style called 'Venetian Gothic'. At 185/915639 is
the old tuckingmill, its waterwheel still in position and, just to the
south of it, the old workhouse, built in 1840 and now The Retreat.
At 185/888646 is Lawry's Mill, Nanskeval.

ST DAY

Little wonder that this old mining town was once called 'the
mining capital of Cornwall' for it is in the parish of Gwennap and in
1841 the parish had a population of 10,800, second only in Cornwall
to Madron at 11,100 which included all Penzance. It lies on the
western edge of an area approaching 1,500 acres (2¼ sq miles) and
centred at 190/750425 that was, in the mid-nineteenth century, the
richest copper-mining district in the old world.

The whole district is redolent of its great mining past: huge stone
engine houses adjoin deep shafts and the landscape has the terrace
houses of its miners and larger dwellings for their 'captains'.

The great mines here were Consolidated, Clifford Amalgamated
and United Mines, with shafts that went down 1,800ft; Clifford
Amalgamated alone employing 1,300 and yielding a profit over
£1,100,000 in the half-century after Waterloo.

The Commissioners Church of 1828 in late Georgian 'Gothick',
and erected for what was then a bustling boom town, 'looks over a
landscape of deserted mines, like so many monuments to the passing

of human achievement, more deeply moving than the artificial picturesque mementos in 18th century gardens' (Pevsner, *Cornwall*).

At 190/785435, see the great engine house of Wheal Unity Wood and between 190/743422 and 758422, the vast area of dereliction and old engine houses of the Consolidated Mines abandoned in 1857.

ST DENNIS

To the south-west of the village, at 185/945568, is the Parkandillack engine house in excellent preservation containing the great 50in beam pumping-engine from the Copperhouse Foundry in 1852 and which had a working life of a century. Its 'hallmark' is the dog's paw marks inadvertently cast on the beam. It is a complete unit including the Cornish boilers, and now works by compressed air as a historical relic. Just to the west of the building is a circular buttonhole launder and extensive micas.

At 185/949572 are the remains of Gullies Wharf at Hendra Prazey, the southern terminus of Treffry's first tramway to Newquay Harbour and to where china clay from Hendra Downs Clay Works was trammed. In particular see the old stone-faced platform and 'cattlecreep' bridge over which the railway ran. The one-time through railway from Burngullow station on the main line now terminates at Gullies, but the most westerly clay works in the area are still served by the branch, 4 miles long, from St Dennis Junction through Retew to Collins Dry at Meledor west of Trethosa, built as late as 1907–12.

ST DOMINIC

This village, 2 miles south-west of Calstock, has been an important centre for the Cornish cherry industry for 150 to 200 years. At 187/415657, see Halton Quay on the west bank of the Tamar, where there still are a group of fine limekilns, once so necessary for local farmers, the last of many such Tamar kilns to be fired.

ST ERTH

At 189/554248 is Tredrea Manor, the home of Davies Gilbert

(1767–1839), Cornwall's outstanding technocrat in the days of the first Industrial Revolution, technical 'adviser' to Trevithick and Jonathan Hornblower, the discoverer of Sir Humphry Davy, and President of the Royal Society. Nearby, at 189/551346, is a piggery, once Battery Mills and owned in 1873 by one Gilbert who specialised in the manufacture of Cornish shovels of iron faced with steel, the furnaces being driven by a waterwheel that has long disappeared.

The parish's most important association with industry lies in its connection with the Treloweth smelting house at 189/543359. Built in the early-eighteenth century, it was the site of Cornwall's first reverberatory furnace and was acquired in 1791 by L. C. Daubuz, whose family continued to manage it until it closed down in 1883 (p 84).

ST GERMANS

At 186/363571 is the old quay of St Germans to which were brought limestone and coal in particular before the railway came from Plymouth in 1859, and where there is a large battery of stone hoppers for discharging into ships' holds. From this quay, in the 1850s, passengers embarked and alighted from steamers on the St Germans–Devonport service. Just north of the quay, is the fine stone GWR viaduct of 1908.

Between 186/375572 and 187/415572, are the traces of the original track of the Cornwall Railway as built in the early 1850s, with traces of the abutments of the timber viaducts at Wivelscombe, Grove and St Germans.

St Germans railway station is an untouched Cornwall Railway structure of 1858, in stucco and 'Tudor' style and should not be destroyed as have other original stations on the Cornwall main line.

ST ISSEY

At Sea Mills (185/921736), at the end of a quiet lane on Little Petherick Creek, there is a curious 4 acre pond enclosed by a long wall built after the North Cornish 'hedge' tradition, ie slate rubble set vertically in courses. At its north-eastern end are two sluices and

Q

adjacent to them the foundations of one of Cornwall's twelve tide-mills, the arched opening for the shaft still in situ. It was a stone-built mill of five floors and the pond fed a large 30ft × 4ft wheel driving six pairs of stones. It had gone by 1905.

ST IVES

Its importance as a port is seen in the completion of a harbour in 1770, designed by John Smeaton, at the end of which is still the elegant lighthouse of 1830. The pier was extended in the late 1880s and at its extremity is an iron lighthouse provided by Stothert & Pitt in 1890. To the north is a short granite pier or breakwater built 1866–7, a further pier completing the south side of the harbour.

It was once a fishing town of considerable importance (p 196) but in 1924 the industry employed only 100 workers, a fifth of the number of a quarter of a century before. Today it is almost wholly a holiday resort.

To see evidence of its former industry, visit the splendid museum at Wheal Dream just south of The Island where there is a photographic record of St Ives' fishing and mining history, together with a great many exhibits collected locally.

ST JUST-IN-PENWITH

For details of sites in this area see Chapter Four, pp 57–68.

ST MAWES

At 190/848330 is the pier rebuilt in 1873 by the St Mawes Harbour Company and at Polwarth (190/855331) is Peter's shipbuilding yard, makers of pilot-gigs since 1790 and still functioning. The original saw-pit is extant. Its oldest boat, a gig built in 1812, is still afloat at Newquay.

ST MINVER

On Carlyon Hill at 185/958753 is the tower of the old St Minver windmill, 30ft high and a noted landmark.

ST PINNOCK

The loftiest of all railway viaducts in Cornwall and the finest remaining of the works of Brunel (excluding Saltash), St Pinnock viaduct (186/178638) is 151ft high and its iron-girder bridge of 1882 is carried on the brown-slate piers of Westwood Quarry stone, selected by Brunel himself and built 1854–5. Half a mile to the west is the only other similar viaduct, but not so high, the East Largin 1855–86. Along this remarkable stretch of railway line on the south side of the Glynn Valley, there are five other notable stone viaducts, all rebuilt from the original timbered bridges between 1877–97. They lie between 186/135650 and 186/195647 and are named Penadlake, Clinnick, Derrycombe, West Largin and Westwood.

ST STEPHEN-IN-BRANNEL

At Goonvean Clay Works (185/947552) is the 50in Cornish beam pumping-engine of 1863 moved here in 1910 from a mine at St Agnes; one of the eight surviving engines in Cornwall out of a total of 650 working about 1860. The new beam, installed in 1928, was made by Holman's Foundry, Camborne, and was perhaps the last to be made in Britain.

At 185/950545 are the derelict remains of what was the finest complex of water-powered china-stone grinding mills in Cornwall, operated by Thomas Olver & Co Ltd (pp 118–19).

SALTASH

Tin mining on the western side of Dartmoor brought about the rise of Tavistock as the industry's market eight centuries ago. From there the tin was taken for export to a place on the Cornish side of the Tamar called Esse, later Saltash. Its main quays were used for centuries for bringing in coal, timber, machinery, and lime for fertilising the land. Refined tin, copper ore and huge quantities of granite were exported, a trade continuing until 1914. Wearde Quay (187/425577) is now grass covered and beginning to break up, as is the quay at Moditonham (187/420612) which was the outlet for the market gardens of Botus Fleming, famous for its cherries, one variety being the Green Stem Rumbullion.

At Antony Passage (187/415573) are the remains of the last tide mill in Cornwall. It bears the inscription 'FB RB AB 1613' over the arch to the first floor, and '1866' over a ground-floor arch, but *The Black Prince's Register* gives 1465 as the date when stone was brought for the dam by barge. The initials are those of Frederick, Richard and Abraham Buller, but it became the property of the Pearce family in 1863. They rebuilt it three years later and it went out of use about twenty years afterwards. There were four wooden wheels about 12ft diameter × 3ft wide, driven by water impounded in a 8½ acre pond whose banks still exist. The quay here can just be traced.

The glory of Saltash is the Royal Albert Bridge spanning the Tamar where it is 1,100ft wide (p 108). First conceived by Brunel in the late 1840s, the main construction work was started in 1853 and by July 1858 the first of the two great iron trusses was complete, the second at the end of March 1859. Its cost was only £225,000, and its total length 2,200ft. The first through train from Plymouth to Truro travelled across the bridge on 11 April 1859 and the official opening was by HRH Prince Albert on 2 May. Brunel was seriously ill in Rome on that occasion, but later that month he was drawn slowly across it lying on a couch on a flat truck. He died four months later. His railway station of 1858 survives.

SCORRIER

Part of the mining parish of Gwennap, this area is scored with remains of great metal mines. Through here there ran the first railway in Cornwall, the Poldice Tramway, its southern terminus at Croft-handy (190/739425) and then running via Scorrier railway station, Mawla (190/702458) and Bridge to the harbour at Portreath. At the west end of the now disused railway station, see the bridge built by the West Cornwall Railway about 1851–2 to take their standard-gauge line on embankment over the Poldice Tramway, an ingeniously constructed skew-arch tunnel in brick nearly 40ft long and at its eastern end a large cast-iron girder stamped 'BRYMBO 1865'—Brymbo being the foundry in North Wales then managed by one of the Darbys of Coalbrookdale.

At 190/723452 is the great Doctor's Shaft engine house of the North Treskerby tin and copper mine, one of several it is hoped to preserve as an industrial monument and, centred around 190/710445, the stamps, pumping and whim engine houses of Wheal Peevor (c 1875) but not abandoned until the end of World War I.

SENNEN COVE

At 189/350264, this is the most westerly harbour in south-west England, and a pier built in 1908 has a plaque recording the gratitude of the inhabitants to a Col Williams of St Ives who did so much to raise the money for it. Nearby is an old circular stone building, the upper part of the walls sheathed in black tarred weatherboarding, the conical roof covered with scantles (small Delabole slates set in mortar) which was the capstan house for hauling small boats up the beach and stone-paved slip.

STICKER

An area of mining activity with remains of a number of mines particularly: Polgooth (190/000505) which was producing tin until the mid-1880s and its engine house; Ventonwyn Mine (190/960497) which was sold up in May 1907 for £740, its engine house having a 36in pumping and stamping engine; and the several engine houses of St Austell Consols Mine that over a period of thirty-five years up to 1880 produced copper, tin, lead, nickel, cobalt, uranium and arsenic ores, albeit in small quantities.

There are also remains at Polgooth Mine of old timber-built stamps, said to have been made from the timbering of Brunel's Gover Viaduct when it was replaced by the stone one in 1898.

STITHIANS

At 190/737365 is Phillips' water-powered mill, in production until 1966 with a fine 18ft × 4ft wheel.

TORPOINT

The town has developed entirely since the advent of the Industrial Revolution having only four or five houses in 1780, about 200 forty years later and a population of 2,000 by 1870. The ferry to Devonport started in July 1791; but J. M. Rendel, civil engineer, designed and built the chain ferry with steam paddle-boats that started in 1834. The ferry terminal buildings of granite were built during the past fifty years by Cornwall CC. Adjacent to this terminal are the buildings of the old Torpoint Gas Company; their closure on 30 September 1967 after eighty-three years was remarkable in that it was the last hand-fired gasmaking plant in England.

At 187/440549 are the buildings and coal wharf of W. J. Reynolds Ltd, tug masters, who own a fleet of steam tugs still in constant use for shipping on the Hamoaze.

TOWEDNACK

To the north of Cripple's Ease at 189/501369 can be seen the extensive remains of Giew or South Providence Mine that was worked exclusively for tin from 1871 to 1923, while close by is part of the engine house of a much older mine, Wheal Reeth. Giew is interesting because, in a relatively compact space, one may survey all the processes of the winning of tin (pp 69-70). Giew House was once the home of a mine captain.

At Plenderleath, at 189/495377, is an old china-clay works, the water from the deep pit still fed to the Unigate Creamery 4 miles away at St Erth station through the original slurry pipe that delivered clay to the dry at the station.

TRESILLIAN

Until the 1930s, the long wooded creek called Tresillian River connecting Tresillian (190/865465) with the Truro River at Malpas, saw ketches and schooners and other vessels bringing in grain for the maltings (buildings extant), roadstone for highways, coal and timber, to its quay.

TRURO

The cathedral city and administrative capital of Cornwall would not appear today to have many links with the county's industrial past, but it was once a stannary town, while the collection of warehouses on its quay indicates its importance as a port whence white tin was taken for the pewter trade in London. One warehouse was a candle factory. In fact, Truro was the centre of the tin-smelting industry, and three smelting houses, in one form or another, still survive. Truro smelting house, begun in 1816, occupied a site immediately east of the present-day St Austell Street, close by the navigable head of the River Allen where it entered Truro River, and its lines can still be detected in Trafalgar Square. The Carvedras smelter, now a warehouse and not appreciably changed apart from the stacks, lies east of the railway station and almost under the great viaduct of 1904, alongside which lie the piers of Brunel's original timber viaduct. The Calenick smelter is at 190/821431, a mile south of the town at the navigable head of a creek branching westwards from the Fal, but only its clock tower still remains.

The fine museum of the Royal Institution of Cornwall (founded 1818) in River Street contains a wealth of material about Cornwall's industrial history. There is an excellent diorama of a china-clay working; photographs of timber viaducts; and wooden salt scoops, shovels, and barrel branding-irons from Newquay fish cellars.

At Boscawen Bridge are the nineteenth-century sail and tent-making works of W. Penrose & Son, designed by Silvanus Trevail.

TYWARDREATH

At 185/085560 are remains of the great Fowey Consols Mine, the company to work it having been formed in 1813. J. T. Treffry and others purchased it in 1822 and the nearby Lanescot Mine in 1836. By the 1840s, 1,800 workers were employed and the mine had seven large engines and thirteen waterwheels for which the water came from Molinnis Moors 4½ miles to the north-west via the leat and Treffry's aqueduct at Luxulyan (p 109). The mine had finished by 1867: but at its peak it had seventeen waterwheels supplying nearly 500hp as well as other hydraulic engines. The engine house built for the famous 80in engine is suggested for preservation, as an important industrial monument to Cornwall's mining past.

WADEBRIDGE

From Bradford's Quay on the north-east bank of the wide River Camel here, the granite blocks from De Lank were fashioned and then shipped out for Smeaton's Eddystone lighthouse in the 1750s. Sand of the Camel estuary at Padstow has been described as the richest in Cornwall in carbonate of lime, ie 80 per cent, and up to 100,000 tons a year used at one time to be transported inland as a soil conditioner. One of the reasons for building the first steam railway in Cornwall from Wadebridge in 1834 was to facilitate the carriage of this sea sand to farms. Barges came up from Padstow to discharge sand at Wadebridge, indeed there was a dock capable of holding twenty of them at one time. The sand was discharged into waiting railway trucks and so reached the hinterland.

At the north-west of Harbour Road, at 185/990726 on the bank opposite Bradford's Quay, see the old Town Harbour with its several railway sidings parallel to and end-on to the quay wall, the lines last relaid by the LSWR 1911–16. Diesel shunting-engines still deal with freight wagons on these sidings, loaded with agricultural feeding stuffs and the like consigned from Avonmouth Docks to local merchants. On this quay is a motley collection of buildings of stone, brick, timber and corrugated iron, one a particularly interesting granary of three storeys with a slate mansard roof—early nineteenth century.

For two centuries Bradford's Quay was used for the off-loading of coal, timber and bricks and, in later years, cement from South Wales and timber from the Baltic. F. & J. Martyn established their business here long ago and it continued until very recent years although it has been part of Taylor & Low Ltd of Bristol since 1933. The first ship to navigate the tortuous channel of the Camel after World War II was the German coaster *Flut* in 1955, but all commercial shipping ceased after 25 January 1962 when the last small coaster, the MV *Vectis Isle*, brought in 225 tons of coal from Blyth for Taylor & Low's yard. Even Welsh coal, brought into Padstow's harbour and thence by road to this firm's coal wharf on Bradford's Quay, ceased in May 1970.

The NCR station of 1895 still exists in part but the 1834 B&WR buildings were destroyed in 1969.

The iron foundry of Oatey & Martyn, founded 1847, is no longer used as such, but part has become a 'steam' museum.

Trewornan Bridge (185/987743) is a fine four-arched stone bridge of 1791, across the one-time creek that formerly brought ships up to Chapel Amble at its head, now reduced to a narrow stream.

WENDRON

This district was once the centre of one of the richest tin areas in the county and it abounds in considerable remains.

At 189/675300 are the engine house and stacks of Wheal Ann and Wheal Dream, both parts of what became known as Trumpet Consols. Wheal Ann is of interest since in 1877 its 45in engine worked with a wooden bob, one of the last in Cornwall. To the south-west of Porkellis (189/693335) are the engine houses of Wheal Enys and Basset and Grylls. On the main Helston–Falmouth road are three mine relics of distinction: near Carnebone at 189/702315 the engine house of East Wheal Lovell; at 189/695304 near Manhay the ivy-covered stacks and engine-house ruins of Great Wheal Lovell; and on Retanna Hill, ¾ mile south-west of the Halfway House Inn near the road junction that leads to Gweek, the single stack of Bal Ding Mine that collapsed owing to the slump of the 1860s, caused by the American Civil War.

ZELAH

At 190/792509 see the engine house of West Chiverton lead mine, part of the important Chiverton lead-mining area of the mid-nineteenth century. In 1864 it had an 80in pumping engine; in 1870 it employed 1,000 people and had a main shaft over 700ft deep. It ceased in 1886.

ZENNOR

At 189/454384 is the Wayside Folk Museum which houses a superb collection of exhibits illustrative of the entire industrial life of West Cornwall. Agriculture is represented by banking ploughs, tommyhawks, tubbles, Cornish shovels, spading irons and the like; mining by driving hammers, tampers, rock drills etc; quarrying by jumpers, wedges and feathers for splitting the granite, and chop axes; and fishing by net needles, limpet crooks and lance hooks.

The cottage of the museum should not be overlooked for it contains a perfect example of an open hearth, complete with cooking implements and utensils, a circular stone oven and a large open chimney. At the end of the garden is the mill, virtually intact except for the mill wheel. The rest of the driving mechanism is in situ and consists of two grinding-stones, gearing and a main driving-wheel, the teeth of which were made of apple wood as a deliberate built-in weakness to be easily replaceable if the stones became jammed.

Near the museum may be found two examples of locally quarried stones, underground blowing-houses, remains of old mines like Zennor Consols and, on Zennor Hill, the quarry from which stone was cut for the harbour at Falmouth. Under Zennor Head at Boat Cove (189/448390) are remains of stanchions and windlasses where once the local pilchard fleet operated and near the cove stand the walls of the pressing-house where the fish were pressed.

West of Zennor there are the remains of three copper mines: at 189/438382, in a spectacular position overlooking the Atlantic, is the engine house of the Gurnard's Head Mine; at 189/422625 at the side of the road between Zennor and Morvah are the ruins of the two pumping and winding engine houses of Carn Galver or Rosemergy Mine; and at 189/407359 near the cliff due north of Morvah church may be found the engine house of Morvah Consols. Around all these mines may be discovered traces of leats and wheel-pits dating from the days when the machinery was driven by water power.

Bibliographical Notes

CORNWALL is immensely rich in industrial archaeology and there are a great many books that enable the student to explore its various aspects. As an introduction to industrial archaeology in general, two recent publications of merit are Kenneth Hudson's *Industrial Archaeology* (new edition, John Baker, London, 1966) and Michael Rix, *Industrial Archaeology* (Historical Association 1967). J. P. M. Pannell's *Techniques of Industrial Archaeology* (David & Charles, Newton Abbot, 1966) is written especially for students of the subject. W. H. Curnow's booklet *The Industrial Archaeology of Cornwall* (Tor Mark Press, Truro, 1969) is useful for the county itself, while the archaeology of the one-time concentration of industry around Calstock and Gunnislake has been excellently documented by Frank Booker in *The Industrial Archaeology of the Tamar Valley* (David & Charles, 1967). Equally useful is Michael Tangye's booklet *The History of Portreath* (John Olson, Redruth, 1968). John Allen's *History of Liskeard* (1856) is another useful source.

The many histories of Cornwall are valuable; Richard Carew's *Survey of Cornwall*, first published in 1602, particularly for the information it gives about mining, quarrying and fishing in Elizabethan times; the early nineteenth-century histories by Samuel Lysons (1813), C. S. Gilbert (1820) and Davies Gilbert (1838) which are useful for the period when Cornwall had become an important industrial area; and Murray's *Handbook for Travellers in Devon and Cornwall*, first published in 1850 and whose 1859 edition has just been reprinted by the publishers of this present work. For later in the century, the *Gazetteer of Cornwall*, compiled in 1884 by the Truro

Engineer R. E. Symons, gives much mining and quarrying detail; the *Victoria County History* (1905) has specialist contributions on mining, quarrying, china clay, fishing and agriculture; and *Essays in Cornish History* by the late Charles Henderson (Oxford 1935) contains information on tuckingmill sites. Sir Nicholas Pevsner's *Cornwall* (Buildings of England Series, 2nd edition 1970) is of interest for students of the history of Cornish architecture and buildings, but more particularly is *The Functional Tradition in Early Industrial Buildings* by J. M. Richards (Architectural Press, 1958). For the economic and social historian, *Cornwall in the Age of the Industrial Revolution* by John Rowe (Liverpool University Press, 1953) is highly recommended.

METAL MINING

The literature on Cornwall's historically most important industry is so voluminous that it is only possible to indicate the major source materials. Both the County Record Office and the Royal Institution of Cornwall, each of them located in Truro, hold formidable and unique collections of mining records, as to a lesser extent does the Royal Geological Society of Cornwall, Penzance. The most important work of reference by far, particularly on the technical side, is *The Mining Journal* which first started publishing in 1835, a complete set of which can be consulted in the Redruth Public Library. Much relevant information will also be found in such newspapers as the *Sherborne Mercury*, the *Royal Cornwall Gazette* and the *West Briton*. Students should also consult the published transactions of the following societies for the wealth of specialist information they possess: the Institute of Mining & Metallurgy; the Miners' Association of Devon & Cornwall; the Mining Association of Cornwall; the Royal Institution of Cornwall; and the Royal Geological Society of Cornwall. *The Mining Almanac*, *The Mining Magazine* and *The Mining World* will also be found to be generally useful. *Post Office* and *Kelly's Directories* should not be overlooked for they contain a surprising array of out-of-the-way facts about occupations that have vanished.

Other indispensable authorities are William Pryce's *Mineralogia Cornubiensis* (1778), Robert Hunt's *British Mining* (1887), G. Abbot's *An Essay on the Mines of England* (1835), J. H. Collins' *The Miner in Cornwall and Devon* (1897) and H. T. de la Beche's significant *Report on the Geology of Cornwall, Devon and West Somerset* (1839). As a comprehensive record of about 2,000 mines throughout Cornwall as well as the geology of the Cornish mining field, J. H. Collins, *Observations on the West of England Mining Region* (1912) is of special interest. It should be read in conjunction with a more recent study, that of H. G. Dines, *The Metalliferous Mining Region of South-West England* (1956). The list would not be complete without mentioning a work published in 1908 by an American scholar and which still remains the best authority on the subject, *The Stannaries* by G. Randall Lewis. It was reprinted in 1966 by the publishing house of D. B. Barton of Truro. In the *Post Office Directory of Cornwall* (London, 1873) there are detailed descriptions, with names of personnel, of over 260 working mines.

Within recent years D. B. Barton has established himself, not only as a publisher of books on Cornwall, but as an authority in his own right about metal mining. Since 1960 he has written several major studies that may be regarded as definitive: *The Cornish Beam Engine* (1966), *A History of Tin Mining and Smelting in Cornwall* (1967) and *Essays in Cornish Mining History* (1968). Shorter works that he has written, but models of precision and accuracy of information, are: *A History of Copper Mining in Cornwall and Devon* (1961); *A Guide to the Mines of West Cornwall* (1965); *A Historical Survey of the Mines and Mineral Railways of East Cornwall and West Devon* (1964) and *Historic Cornish Mining Scenes Underground* (1967), based on the photographs of J. C. Burrows of Camborne and Herbert Hughes.

He has also been responsible for publishing several works by other authors, among which may be mentioned: T. R. Harris, *Arthur Woolf (1766–1837), the Cornish Engineer* (1967); H. L. Douch's first-rate study of a single mine, *East Wheal Rose: the History of Cornwall's greatest Lead Mine* (1964); Edmund Vale, *The Harveys of Hayle*

(1966); H. G. Ordish, *Pictorial Survey of Cornish Engine Houses* (1967); and J. H. Trounson, *Historic Cornish Mining Scenes at Surface* (1969). A series of sixteen booklets of studies of individual mines under the general title of *The Mines and Miners of Cornwall*, by the doyen of Cornish mining historians, A. K. Hamilton Jenkin, has been produced in recent years. Nos 1–3 were published by Barton of Truro; nos 4–14 are now from Town & Country Press, Bracknell; and nos 15 and 16 from the Federation of Old Cornwall Societies, Redruth.

Mr Hamilton Jenkin established his reputation with *The Cornish Miner* (1927) which has recently been reprinted. A. C. Todd, *The Cornish Miner in America* (Barton, 1967) contains some account of the emigration of Cornish technology, while his study of Cornwall's premier technocrat, Davies Gilbert, in *Beyond the Blaze* (Barton, 1967) is of some interest for the new material it presents about Richard Trevithick and Jonathan Hornblower, two of Cornwall's foremost mining engineers. For further accounts of the engineers, the student is referred to H. W. Dickinson, *The Cornish Engine* (1951); H. W. Dickinson and A. Titley, *Richard Trevithick, The Engineer and The Man* (1934); and Francis Trevithick's biography of his father, *The Life of Richard Trevithick* (1872). *A Dynasty of Ironfounders the Darby's of Coalbrookdale* by Arthur Raistrick (1953) is a fascinating history of ironfounding and smelting and should be consulted for its reference to Trevithick's work at Coalbrookdale from 1796. L. T. C. Rolt's biography of Richard Trevithick was published under the title *Cornish Giant* (1960). Edith Harper also wrote a biography of Trevithick entitled *Cornish Giant* and published in 1913. For a study of the personalities of many industrial pioneers, *Engineering Heritage* (2 vols, 1963–6, for the Institution of Mechanical Engineers) contains a wealth of information contributed by many specialist writers.

HAYLE

The story of the new industrial town of Hayle in West Cornwall is the story of the remarkable Harvey family. This is told in *The Harveys of Hayle* by Edmund Vale (Barton, Truro, 1966).

CHINA CLAY

The standard up-to-date reference books are Mrs R. M. Barton, *History of the Cornish China-clay Industry* (Barton, Truro, 1966) and *A History of English China Clays* by Kenneth Hudson (David & Charles, 1969), but there are references to this industry in other books already quoted. There are also references to Cornwall in *The Rise of the Staffordshire Potteries* by John Thomas (Adams & Dart, Bath, 1971).

CANALS

Two works of reference are *Canals, Navigable Rivers and Railways in England and Wales* by Joseph Priestley, originally published in 1831 and now available in a Cassell reprint; and Charles Hadfield, *The Canals of South West England* (David & Charles, 1967) which gives the history of all the canals, projected and built, in Cornwall, with considerable detailed information.

RAILWAYS

The development of railways in the British Isles has created an interest for historians over several generations, and the building of 350 miles of them all over Cornwall in the century from 1809 to 1908 is well documented: E. T. MacDermott, *History of the GWR* (1968) originally written 1927–31; Hamilton Ellis, *The South-Western Railway* (1956); and vol 1 of R. A. Williams, *History of the LSWR* (David & Charles, 1968) are three excellent books. The predecessor of the GWR was the Cornwall Railway whose history is to be found in R. J. Woodfin, *The Centenary of the Cornwall Railway* (W. Jefferson, Ely, 1960) and concisely in *The Story of Cornwall's Railways* (Barton, Truro, 1970) and *The Hayle, West Cornwall and Helston Railways* by

G. H. Anthony (Oakwood Press, Lingfield, Surrey, 1969). *The Withered Arm* by T. W. E. Roche (Town & Country Press, Bracknell, 1967) is useful for information about the North Cornish lines. D. St J. Thomas, *A Regional History of the Railways of Great Britain; Vol I, The West Country* (3rd edition, David & Charles, 1966) contains information on the trade and population of Cornwall as well as on railways. L. T. C. Rolt's biography *Isambard Kingdom Brunel* (1957) contains an account of the building of the Royal Albert Bridge, Saltash, as does Murray's *Handbook*.

Individual early railways in Cornwall have been the subject of special studies: D. B. Barton, *The Redruth and Chasewater Railway 1824–1915* (Barton, Truro, 1966); R. Crombleholme, *Callington Railways*, with notes on the mines and shipping of the Tamar Valley (Town & Country Press, 1967) and *The Bodmin and Wadebridge Railway* by C. F. D. Whetmath with photos and maps from the same publisher 1967. Cornwall's third railway, *The Pentewan 1829–1918*, has been documented by M. J. T. Lewis (Barton, 1960). The mining development on the west bank of the Tamar brought about new railway construction there, told in D. B. Barton, *Historical Survey of the Mines and Mineral Railways of East Cornwall* (1964).

ROADS

Magna Brittania by David and Samuel Lysons (1814) is a source of information about the mail-coach routes in Cornwall in Regency times, whilst *Old Cornish Bridges* by Charles Henderson and Henry Coates (Simpkin Marshall, London, 1928) is a vivid historical record with many photographs of road bridges then existing. Cyril Noall, *Cornish Mail and Stage Coaches* (Barton, Truro, 1964) is of considerable value to students of road transport.

SHIPPING AND HARBOURS

Two informative books on Cornish harbours are *Cornish Harbours*

R

by R. J. Roddis (Christopher Johnson, 1951) and more recently *Ports and Harbours of Cornwall* by R. Pearse (H. Warne, St Austell, 1963) which covers a period of 800 years. Grahame Farr's book *West Country Passenger Steamers* (David & Charles, 1967) is useful for its chapter on the Scilly run and the Hayle to Bristol service 1831–1914. Basil Greenhill, *The Merchant Schooners* (2 vols, David & Charles, 1957) gives much detail about Cornish sailing vessels.

LIGHTHOUSES

The fascinating history of the construction of the Cornish light-houses and the work of Trinity House who has maintained them for so long is to be found in several books. The student will find useful J. P. Bowen, *British Lighthouses* (1947); J. Grosvenor, *Trinity House* (1959); Cyril Noall, *Cornish Lights and Wrecks* (Barton, Truro, 1968); and Frederick Majdalany, *The Red Rocks of Eddystone* (1954) which is a vivid history of all the lighthouses built on that reef, 13 miles off the Cornish coast, since 1698.

WIRELESS

Those who would learn more of the work of Guglielmo Marconi and his colleagues who pioneered wireless in Cornwall during the period 1900–34, may obtain from the Marconi Company at Chelms-ford two booklets, no 6 *Imperial and International Wireless Communications 1909–46* and no 7 *A Chapter of Marconi's History, The Story of Poldhu*.

QUARRYING

Memoirs of the Geological Survey SW England (HMSO, 1953); *The Geology of Falmouth and Truro and of the Mining Districts of Camborne and Redruth* by J. Hill and D. A. MacAlister (HMSO, 1906); together with R. M. Barton, *An Introduction to the Geology of Cornwall*

(Barton, Truro, 1964) are three particularly useful works of reference.

WIND AND WATER MILLS

The standard and only textbook on windmills in Cornwall is *Cornish Windmills* by H. L. Douch (Blackford, Truro, 1964). Available for reference at the Royal Institution of Cornwall is the research material on Cornish watermills compiled in the 1940s and 1950s by the late Arthur Saundry of Penzance. There are over 150 photographs made during this period together with earlier ones.

FUSE MAKING

Bickford Smith & Co Ltd published a centenary history of the firm in 1931 containing useful information about methods and personalities connected with the industry since 1831.

MAPS

The *Historian's Guide to Ordnance Survey Maps* by J. B. Harley (National Council of Social Service, 1964) has much for those working in the field of historical geography, and of inestimable value to students of Cornish industrial archaeology are the 6in and 25in scale maps of the Ordnance Survey in the First Edition surveyed in the 1870–80s. Now rare, but equally of value, are the large 1:500th scale maps of towns of over 5,000 population in 1871, that were surveyed during the same period.

David & Charles have recently reprinted all ninety-seven sheets of the first edition of the one-inch Ordnance Survey for England & Wales: the relevant sheets for Cornwall are 82 (Bideford, surveyed 1803–7); 89 (Hartland Point and Camelford, 1805–10); 90 (Tavistock, 1803–7); 95 (Penzance, 1809); 96 (Truro and Lizard Head, 1809–11); 97 (Plymouth, 1803–5).

Acknowledgements

THE preparation of this book has been beset by unusual difficulties. Dr Todd had barely finished Chapter Two when he was invited to be a Visiting Professor at the University of Arizona; he subsequently wrote Chapters Three and Four in California and Chapter One in Hong Kong. Mr Laws gallantly undertook to complete the research and finish the book; he has written Chapters Six to Nine and assisted with Chapter One. Mr Wigley kindly contributed the material on Hayle in Chapter Five. The Gazetteer is the joint effort of the principal authors, and Mr Laws wrote the Bibliographical Notes.

The book, that has required so much detailed research into the history of various industries, could never have been written without the help of several hundred individuals as well as organisations, authorities and firms. To all of them the authors are extremely grateful, and especially to Mrs F. Nankivell.

We wish to thank in particular Mr Peter Hull, the Cornwall County Archivist and his staff; Mr H. L. Douch, Curator of the Royal Institution of Cornwall; the Penzance Corporation Librarian and his staff who have so willingly given much help; the Penzance Library and its Librarian Mrs Muriel Harvey for splendid facilities for research; the libraries of the Falmouth Corporation, the Camborne–Redruth UDC and the Cornwall CC; the Cornwall Archaeological Society for promoting an interest in industrial archaeology and, not least, many students in adult classes all over Cornwall who have produced some surprising information.

Many officers of local authorities have been very helpful, in particular Mr George Channon, Surveyor to Wadebridge & Padstow RDC; the borough surveyors at Penzance, Falmouth, Penryn and St Austell-with-Fowey; Mr Charles Ball, Surveyor to Bude–Stratton

UDC and Miss Marie Johns of the Torpoint UDC clerk's department.

Individuals to whom our thanks are due for much local information include Mr Douglas Vosper of Saltash; Mr E. Bate Venning of Launceston; Mr Stewart Crispin of Kew, London. We thank Mr W. H. Paynter for assistance about Liskeard and Miss Sybil Pomeroy of Liskeard for maps and other valuable help; Mr A. Skewes of Camborne and Mr P. J. T. Barbary of Slough for invaluable help on the fuse industry; Mrs J. P. Hooper of Pentewan for information about the old port of Pentewan; Mr T. R. Harris for assistance about Cornish foundries and Mr Rex Wailes, late Director of the National Survey of Industrial Monuments for his encouragement and the gift of his unbounded knowledge gained over half a century of research. We are grateful to the Rt Hon Lord Arwyn and the Rt Hon Harold Wilson for their assistance in connection with the explosives industry.

In connection with the china-clay industry, we wish to thank not only English Clays Lovering Pochin & Co Ltd, Mr John Skelton, Mr Murray Gowan and Mr George Starke for so much practical help; but also the Goonvean & Rostowrack China Clay Co Ltd and Messrs J. R. Goldsworthy and Courtenay Smales. For information on stone quarrying our thanks are due to the Old Delabole Slate Co Ltd and Mr J. W. P. Coggon; Mr Creswell Spargo of H. Spargo (Trolvis) Ltd, Long Downs; Mr Cyril Leese of Bristol & the West of England Road Metal Co Ltd, Porthoustock. For her research into the serpentine industry we are grateful to Miss Ruth Phillips of Goldsithney. For the loan of the late Arthur Saundry's typescript and photographs of Cornish watermills, our thanks go to Mr Frank Trewhella of Leedstown.

The subject of communications in all its forms has necessitated a great deal of research and for help in this we are grateful to Mr Jack Kingston of Torpoint; Mr George Anthony of Plympton; the Western Region of British Railways and Mr E. H. Fowkes, Archivist at Paddington; Mr Lloyd Goodman of Launceston; the Rev Peter Sanderson, Vicar of Poundstock and Mr Ian Ballantyne of Stratton for their assistance in connection with the North Cornwall Railway; Western Union International Inc, the Marconi Company Ltd and Mr Garfield Gilbert of Mullion for research and information on cables and radio; officers of the South Western Gas Board and Mr Wilfred Broad of Callington for information about the history of the gas industry in Cornwall; Mr E. R. Shaw and others for their help in compiling the history of the electricity supply; Mr R. P. Truscott of the Cornwall county surveyor's department and Miss M. E. Philbrick of Carnon Downs for their help on historic bridges and the turnpike trusts; and the officers of the Trinity House Depot at Penzance for research about the Cornish lighthouses.

Finally, our special thanks to Mary and Penny who have had the task of deciphering manuscripts for their typewriters.

In respect of the illustrations for the book, we are grateful to those who have lent or given photographs. They are: Mr J. R. Goldsworthy, Mr Rex Wailes, the Metropolitan Water Board, Old Delabole Slate Co Ltd, Bude–Stratton Urban District Council, Mr Stewart Crispin, Cornish De Lank Granite Quarries Company, Mr John Curtis of Falmouth, Rev Peter Sanderson, Mr Ray Vine of East Grinstead, the late Mr W. Brookes, Messrs J. Bennetts & Sons of Camborne and the professional photographer Mr David Wills of Pendeen, who has been particularly generous. We also thank Mr Charles Woolf of Newquay for taking the photograph of Hingham Mill and of the Treffry Aqueduct. The photograph of the Royal Albert Bridge was taken by Frith of Reigate.

A Note from the Publisher

THERE are many other books in the David & Charles list which will appeal to those who have enjoyed this one. We have for instance books including accounts of all the railways and of all the canals in Cornwall. But there are three titles we would especially recommend.

The first is Frank Booker's *The Industrial Archaeology of the Tamar Valley*. Although in a sense an extension of the Cornish mining area, the Tamar Valley (Cornish on one side and Devon—with Devon Great Consols and Morwellham Quay, now an industrial museum piece—on the other) has a distinctive flavour of its own, and Mr Booker's book has been highly praised, not merely for doing justice to an exciting subject but for being one of the best-researched and most colourfully executed works so far published on industrial history.

Then, going inland for many miles from Bude, across the poor plateauland of north-east Cornwall and north-west Devon to Launceston and Holsworthy, was that extraordinary engineering work, the Bude Canal, half a canal, half a railway, built partly with Government money mainly to carry sea sand rich in lime to tame the sour soil. *The Bude Canal*, by Helen Harris and Monica Ellis, tells the strange tale in full detail.

Finally, a book for which we have an especially warm spot is our reprint of Murray's *Handbook for Devon and Cornwall*, 1859. In those days guide-books objectively reported everything that might interest the curious visitor, and before the rise of the conventional Cornish tourist industry visitors were indeed concerned to know about the mines, the fisheries, the ways in which people worked and played and how they differed from those in the rest of the country. We ourselves have made extensive use of the work over many years and a copy taken in the car is guaranteed to enrich one's understanding of just how great an industrial complex Cornwall once supported, how totally un-English the Cornish were.

Index

References to illustrations are printed in italics